With eternal thanks to my parents
David and Georgia Spradley
who introduced me to Jesus Christ
and taught me His ways.

PREFACE

Purpose and Use of This Study

Whenever we want to know a person better, we have to spend time with her. We have to listen to her words and heart, asking questions to clarify things we don't understand. To the extent we listen, interact, and spend time with someone, to that extent we come to know the person. The same is true in our relationship with God. We must listen to Him, interact with Him, spend time with Him. But with God we must go one step further. We must also obey Him if we are to know Him and have a growing relationship with Him (John 14:21).

Purpose

This study has been written to assist you in coming to know God better and to help you in your relationship with Him. The beautiful result in your life from such knowing and growing will be transformation into His image (2 Corinthians 3:18).

Basic Format

Each lesson has been divided into five studies (like five "devotionals") to encourage you to spend time daily with God in His Word. Each section follows a basic format to help you listen to what God says in His Word and to interact with Him and to respond to Him.

WOMEN'S BIBLE STUDIES

by Ruth Spradley

STANDARD PUBLISHING
Cincinnati, Ohio   39932

Library of Congress Cataloging-in-Publication Data

Spradley, Ruth.
    Women's Bible studies. Colossians.

        1. Bible. N. T. Colossians – Text-books.   I. Title.
BS2715.5.S67   1987   227'.7'0076   86-23029
ISBN 0-87403-232-6

First, each section begins with a general reading of the whole passage being studied (approximately 10-12 verses). This helps you to remember the entire context before zeroing in on the specific verses.

The questions that follow usually proceed in a simple progression. They are designed to answer the following basic questions:

1. What are the basic facts or statements of the verse or verses? What does this verse say? (Observation)

2. What do these facts mean? This may include definitions, thoughts from other Scriptures, comparisons with other passages, illustrations from the Old Testament, etc. (Interpretation)

3. What do these truths mean to me? These are the times to stop and meditate on the truths learned. Chew on them a little, talk with God about them, seeking his wisdom and insight. (Personalization)

4. What is my response to these truths, to God? (Application) This can take a variety of forms.

   (a) Praise and thanks to God for who He is and what He's done based on the truths you've learned.

   (b) Confession of sin when you have not lived in light of the truths of Scripture (1 John 1:9). This is an important time. Often when we see our failure in light of God's truth, we respond in one of two ways:

      (1) We pass it off as impossible to achieve, so therefore we don't

have to take it seriously, or

(2) We get down on ourselves for our failure and walk around depressed under a load of guilt.

But God's way is neither of these. He desires a humble heart willing to confess sin and to accept His forgiveness, a heart that can experience His power as we step by step learn obedience to Him. (Though it may seem like we take "three steps forward and two steps back.")

Remember, God knows your weaknesses, and He is merciful to you. He is also committed to working His truth into your experience (Psalm 103:10-14; Romans 8:29; Philippians 2:13).

(c) Practical steps you can take to be obedient to God's Word.

Practical Consideration

1. The questions in this study are based on the New American Standard Version.

2. When verses are listed vertically, an answer is to be found in each passage.

3. When Scriptures are listed horizontally, the truths from the passages are to be taken as a whole. A summary answer is desired.

4. Cross-references (cf.) are in parentheses and are optional. They either add further insight, or they are a repetition of the same truth in other verses.

5. The questions with an asterisk (*) of each study are optional. Sometimes they are more difficult. They are added for the person who desires a more extensive study.

CONTENTS

Page

1. Introduction   9

2. Knowing God's Will 23

3. The Preeminent Christ 35

4. The Glorious Mystery 47

5. Whose Captive Are You? 59

6. True Spirituality, Part 1 73

7. True Spirituality, Part 2 87

8. True Spirituality, Part 3 99

9. True Spirituality, Part 4 113

10. Three Spiritual Essentials 125

   Guidelines for Leaders 133

1 Paul, an apostle of Jesus Christ by the will of God, and Timothy our brother,

2 to the saints and faithful brethren in Christ who are at Colossae: Grace to you and peace from God our Father.

3 We give thanks to God, the Father of our Lord Jesus Christ, praying always for you,

4 since we heard of your faith in Christ Jesus and the love which you have for all the saints;

5 because of the hope laid up for you in heaven, of which you previously heard in the word of truth, the gospel,

6 which has come to you, just as in all the world also it is constantly bearing fruit and increasing, even as it has been doing in you also since the day you heard of it and understood the grace of God in truth;

7 just as you learned it from Epaphras, our beloved fellow bond-servant, who is a faithful servant of Christ on our behalf,

8 and he also informed us of your love in the Spirit.

1234567 8910 11 12

INTRODUCTION

Colossians 1:1-8

Change is the name of the game in this century. We've gone from horses and buggies to turbo charged engines, from the Wright brothers to space shuttles, from telegraph to worldwide direct dialing. The list could go on and on. But the greatest change in our society in this century has been internal. We've gone from a culture based on the Judeo-Christian tradition to one based on humanism. It didn't happen overnight, just as none of the external changes did. But step by step it happened, though most of us were not aware of it.

Humanism now pervades our educational, judicial, and political systems, and it continually bombards us through every form of the mass media. Christians often think like humanists because they are unaware of the spiritual battle being waged constantly for the control of our minds and lives. They have drifted with a society that they thought was "Christian," and in so doing they have often become humanists in practice. This is an absolute tragedy.

If we take a look at the basic tenets of humanism, we'll discover why the present situation is so tragic. First, a humanist is an atheist. There is no God creating, but a universe self-existing. There is no room for any divine purpose or providence in the affairs of men. Man is his own god, left to himself to do and accomplish all. There is no higher authority than himself. Second, a humanist is an evolutionist. He believes man, his culture, and his physical environment have continually evolved and will continue to do so without supernatural intervention. All behavior and change are due to biological and environmental forces. Third, a humanist holds that there are no absolute standards or morals. Man is his own standard. All ethics depend upon the situation. Tolerance is a key virtue. Fourth, a humanist believes that life has meaning only as one creates and develops one's own future. Self-improvement and personal fulfillment in this world are the ends he seeks, for there is no life after death. Man is considered basically good, so the less restraints he encounters, and the more freedom of expression he is allowed, makes for "the best of all possible worlds."

The basic beliefs of humanism are the underlying cause for the direction our society is going. Feelings rather than responsibilities are what control a person's life. What feels good, what satisfies me, is what is right for me. As it was sung in *You Light Up My Life,* "How can it be wrong when it feels so right." Acceptance of abortion, homosexuality, easy divorce, sexual permissiveness are all outgrowths of the humanistic philosophy that has enveloped our culture.

Christians have been so influenced by our culture that we often try to incorporate humanism into our Christianity. My salvation and walk with God are for the purpose of *my* happiness and fulfillment. Yet God says I'm created and redeemed to bring glory to Him. The absolutes and authority of Scripture are dodged because one doesn't "feel" that they are fair or apply to them. Again, the list could go on and on.

If we are going to be Biblical Christians, we must have Biblical mindsets. Jesus Christ, not ourselves, must be first in everything. We must know Him. We must know who He is, who we are in Him, and what our lies are to be as a result.

Colossians can instruct us here. Paul wrote this letter to a group of Christians who needed to stand strong against the attacks of the heretics in their society. A combination of Gnosticism, Judaistic ceremonialism, and asceticism threatened their Biblical walk with God. Gnosticism said that Jesus Christ was only one of many mediating spirits between God and man. Each added wisdom and knowledge in reaching the fulness of God. Judaistic ceremonialism said that one still needed ritual observances to please God. Asceticism said one had to be severe with oneself to overcome the flesh.

Paul proclaims to the Colossians that Christ is the answer to every attack. He is preeminent, His death was theirs, and His life is theirs. In Him they have everything. In Him they could stand strong.

We do not know if Paul ever visited the Colossian church (located in Asia Minor), but he had heard from Epaphras of their strong Christian faith. He had also heard what they were up against. So he wrote them this letter to help them think and live according to God's Word.

It can do the same for us. May God transform you by His spirit through the renewing of your mind as you study Colossians. And Jesus Christ may become all in all to you in a deeper way than ever before.

Study 1 – *Overview*

1. Read the introduction. Underline what stands out to you.

2. Read through Colossians in one sitting, asking God to minister His Word to your heart.

3. What ministered to you most from your reading?

Study 2 – *Salutation* (1:1, 2)

1. Read Colossians 1:1-8.

2. Who wrote the letter? (Verse 1)

3. (a) Why was Paul an apostle? (Verse 1)

   (b) Why could he claim this (3a)?
       Galatians 1:13-17 (especially verse 15;
       cf. Acts 26:8-20; 1 Corinthians 15:8-10)

   *(c) Compare what you learned in 3b with
       Romans 9:6-24.

   (d) Meditate on what you've learned. What
       insights have you gained about God and
       His will?

   (e) Praise and worship God for the things
       you wrote down in 3d.

4. To whom is the letter addressed? (Verse 2)

5. (a) Who are "saints"? 2 Thessalonians
       1:10; (cf. 2 Thessalonians 2:13;
       1 Thessalonians 2:13)

   (b) Are you a "saint"?
       If yes—praise and thank God for His sal-
       vation.
       If no—turn to Romans 10:9, 10 and be
       obedient to it.

6. (a) What are some characteristics of "faithful brethren"?

   2 Samuel 22:22-24

   Job 1:20-22; 2:9, 10; (cf. Isaiah 26:2, 3)

   Matthew 25:14-23

   (b) Review what you've learned. Can you be characterized as a "faithful believer"? How or how not?

   (c) Where you have not been faithful, confess it as sin to God, ask His forgiveness, and thank Him for it. Where you have been faithful, give thanks to God for His work in you.

   (d) In light of what you've learned, and asking God for insight, what steps do you need to take to be more faithful?

   (e) Ask God to work what you wrote down in 6d deeply into your life. Thank Him for what He's going to do (Ephesians 3:20).

Study 3 – *God, Our Father* (1:2)

1. Read Colossians 1:1-8.

2. Paul greets the Colossians with his usual expression of desire that they experience God's continued grace and peace in their lives.

3. (a) What does Paul call God in verse 2?

   (b) Why can Paul claim this (3a) for himself and the Colossians? John 1:12, 13.

   (c) Is God your Father?
   If yes—thank Him.
   If no—accept Christ today.

*4. (a) Who is this God who is our Father?

   Isaiah 6:1-4

   Isaiah 40:12-31

   (b) Meditate on what you've learned. Ask God to sink the truth into your heart that He is your Father.

5. (a) What are some of the benefits of being children of the heavenly Father?

   Matthew 7:11

Matthew 10:29-31

Romans 8:14-17

2 Thessalonians 2:16, 17

(b) Meditate on these things. Praise and thank God for them.

6. What meant the most to you from what you've learned about God being your Father? Why? How?

Study 4 – *Faith and Love* (1:3-5)

1. Read Colossians 1:1-8

2. Read verses 3-5 in the New International Version:

   (v. 3)   We always thank God, the Father of our Lord Jesus Christ, when we pray for you,

   (v. 4)   because we have heard of your faith in Christ Jesus and of the love you have for all the saints—

   (v. 5)   the faith and love that spring from the hope that is stored up for you in heaven and that you have already heard about in the word of truth, the gospel.

Use the above verses in answering the questions in this section.

3. (a) What did Paul and Timothy do when they prayed for the Colossians? (Verse 3)

   (b) How often did they do this (3a) when they prayed for them? (Verse 3)

   (c) Why did they do this (3a and b)? (Verse 4)

   (d) Review your answers. Why would the things you wrote down in 3c mean so much to Paul and Timothy?
   1 John 3:23 (cf. John 14:21)

4. (a) What caused the Colossians' faith and love? (Verse 5)

   (b) What is this (4a)?
   1 Peter 1:3-5

   (c) Where does one learn these things (4a and b)? (Verse 5b)

5. (a) Meditate on what you've learned.

   (b) Explain the Christian life from what you've learned in this section.

   (c) How is this (5b) different from what you learned about humanism in the introduction.

   (d) Which one does your life reflect? How?

   (e) Praise God for the ways in which your life reflects your relationship to Christ. Confess as sin to God those ways which do not, asking His forgiveness, and thanking Him for it. Ask God to work in you in these areas. Be sure and thank Him for what He's going to do (Ephesians 3:20).

Study 5 – *The Gospel* (1:6-8)

1. Read Colossians 1:1-8.

2. What does verse 6 declare the gospel had done and was doing? (Verse 6)

3. What kind of fruit does the gospel bear in our lives?
   Ephesians 5:9, 10 (cf. Philippians 1:11)
   Galatians 5:22, 23

4. (a) How does the gospel increase (bear fruit) through our lives?
       2 Corinthians 5:18-20

   (b) Why are we to do this (4a)?
       Matthew 28:18-20
       2 Peter 3:9

5. (a) What must we understand if the gospel is to bear fruit in and through our lives? (Verse 6)

   (b) Why is this (5a) so?
       John 15:5

6. (a) Meditate on what you've learned in questions 2-5. What further understanding of the Christian life have you gained from these truths?

   (b) How is this (6a) different from what you learned about humanism in the introduction?

(c) Which one does your life reflect? How or how not?

(d) Again praise and thank God for the ways in which your life reflects Christ. Confess as sin the areas where human- ism has dominated, ask His forgiveness, and thank Him for it. Ask God to work in your life that you might more and more reflect His truth and not be swayed by humanistic thought.

7. (a) Who taught the Colossians the gospel? (Verse 7)

(b) What kind of person was he? (Verses 7, 8)

Colossians 4:12, 13

*(c) What relationship do you see between the character of the person who taught the Colossians about Christ and the quality of their walk with God?

(d) Is there anyone who you'd like to learn from? Why not ask them to spend some time with you and share their Christian life with you?

(e) Is there anyone with whom you could share your walk with God? Why not make it a point to spend some time with them.

9 For this reason also, since the day we heard of it, we have not ceased to pray for you and to ask that you may be filled with the knowledge of His will in all spiritual wisdom and understanding,

10 so that you may walk in a manner worthy of the Lord, to please Him in all respects, bearing fruit in every good work and increasing in the knowledge of God;

11 strengthened with all power, according to His glorious might, for the attaining of all steadfastness and patience; joyously

12 giving thanks to the Father, who has qualified us to share in the inheritance of the saints in light.

13 For He delivered us from the domain of darkness, and transferred us to the kingdom of His beloved Son,

14 in whom we have redemption, the forgiveness of sins.

1 2 3 4 5 6 7
8 9 10 11 12

KNOWING GOD'S WILL

Colossians 1:9-14

One of the most encouraging things in our Christian life is to know that someone is praying for us. If we're experiencing stressful circumstances, medical difficulties, financial problems, marital conflicts, rebellious children, etc., it buoys our spirits just to know other Christians are lifting us up before the Father. This is not empty encouragement, for God has promised to answer prayer. He uses the prayers of His people in ministering His love, His power, and His grace to our lives.

Paul knew this truth well. He was continually praying for others in the body. But on close examination of his prayers recorded in the New Testament one is struck with their subject matter. Though he was aware of outer circumstances which needed to be brought to the

Father, his overriding concern in prayer was the spiritual well-being of his brothers and sisters in Christ. He was concerned about the depth of their knowledge of God—His love, His power, His person. He was concerned about their experience of God in the nitty-gritty of their lives.

Colossians 1:9-14 is one such prayer. Upon hearing of the Colossian's life in Christ, Paul prayed that they might be filled with the knowledge of God's will. He desired this not so they would be theological giants, but that they might live in a manner worthy of the God who redeemed them. God desires the same for us.

We would do well to examine our prayer life. Are we consumed with temporal needs or do eternal qualities receive their proper priority? Make Colossians 1:9-14 your prayer for yourself and those you love. And may you experience the richness of God in your life.

Study 1 – *Knowing God's Will* (1:9)

1. Read the introduction and Colossians 1:9-14.

   2. (a) Why did Paul pray for the Colossians? (Verse 9)
      Colossians 1:4, 6, 8

      (b) How often did he pray? (Verse 9)

      (c) What did he ask for? (Verse 9)

   3. Define filled and knowledge.

   4. (a) What do you learn about God's will from the following verses?

      John 6:39, 40 (cf. Galatians 1:4; Ephesians 1:5)

      1 Thessalonians 4:3-6

      1 Thessalonians 5:16-18

      James 4:13-15

      1 Peter 2:13-15; 3:17; 4:19

      (b) Meditate on what you've learned. Praise and thank God for His will. Ask Him to convict you of areas in your life which are not conformed to His will. Write down what He shows you.

(c) Confess as sin to God the things He convicted you of in 4b, ask His forgiveness, and thank Him for it.

5. (a) How do we grow in spiritual wisdom and understanding of God's will?

   Psalm 111:10 (cf. John 7:17)

   Romans 12:2

   (b) Meditate on these truths. Prayerfully ask God to show you how to apply these truths to what you wrote down in 4b. Write down what He shows you.

6. Pray verse 9 for yourself.

7. How has your understanding of God's will and its relationship to you grown from your study of this section.

*8. Explain verse 9 in your own words.

9. Begin memorizing Colossians 1:9-14. You have through Lesson 5 to complete it.

Study 2 – *A Worthy Walk, Part 1* (1:10)

1. Read Colossians 1:9-14 again.

2. Why does Paul pray for the Colossians to be filled with the knowledge of God's will in all spiritual wisdom and understanding? (Verse 10a)

3. Why are we to do this? Ephesians 2:19, 22 (cf. 1 Corinthians 6:19, 20)

4. (a) What is the essential ingredient to pleasing God?
        Hebrews 11:6 (cf. John 6:29)
    (b) Why is this (4a) so?
        Romans 5:1 (cf. Ephesians 2:8, 9)
    (c) Are you pleasing to God?

        If yes—thank Him for your relationship to Him.

        If no—in faith turn to Christ for salvation, confessing Him as your Lord, and believing in your heart that God raised Him from the dead (Romans 10:9, 10).

5. (a) In verses 10b to 13 Paul lists four ingredients of a worthy walk. What is the first one listed in verse 10b?
    (b) How do we bear fruit?
        John 15:4, 5
    (c) Why is it important to bear fruit?
        John 15:8
    (d) Why can we bear fruit in every good work?
        Ephesians 2:10

(e) Why is it important to have good works to please God?
James 2:26

*(f) How is knowing God's will (v. 9) related to bearing fruit in every good work?
James 1:22-25

6. (a) What is the second ingredient of a worthy walk listed in verse 10?

(b) How do we do this (6a)?
John 14:21

(c) Why is this (6a) important to a worthy walk?
2 Corinthians 3:18

*(d) What do you learn about increasing in the knowledge of God from the life of Job?
Job 1:2; 32:1-6; 33:8-13; 42:16 (cf. 38—41)

7. (a) Meditate on what you've learned. How has your understanding of the Christian life grown from what you've learned?
(b) Are there any steps you need to take so that you might bear fruit or increase in the knowledge of God? What?
(c) Pray Colossians 1:9, 10 for yourself. Pray it for a Christian friend or family member.

8. Continue memorizing Colossians 1:9-14.

Study 3 – *A Worthy Walk, Part 2* (1:11)

1. Read Colossians 1:9-14.

2. Write down a difficult situation you are facing and/or a difficult person in your life. Keep these in mind as you study this section.

3. (a) What is the third ingredient of a worthy walk? (Verse 11a)

   (b) How does this (3a) happen?

      Philippians 4:13

   (c) What is this power, this glorious might like?

      Jeremiah 32:17

   (d) Meditate on these truths. Praise and thank God for them. Put in your own words what verse 11a means from what you've learned.

4. Why are we to be strengthened with God's power? (Verse 11b)

5. (a) Steadfastness refers to enduring, persevering in difficult circumstances.

   (b) Patience refers to long-suffering, bearing with difficult people.

6. (a) Why do we need God's power for stead-fastness and patience?
Galatians 5:22, 23; Romans 15:5

(b) How are these developed in our lives?

(c) Why are they important to a worthy walk?
James 1:2-4 (cf. Romans 5:3-5; 1 Peter 1:6, 7)

7. (a) Meditate on these truths. Praise God for His power and might. Thank God for what you wrote down in 2. Pray verse 11 back to God in reference to what you wrote down in 2.

(b) How has your attitude towards what you wrote down in 2 changed because of your study? Why?

*8. (a) How is Christ our perfect example in patience and steadfastness?
Hebrews 12:2, 3

(b) How can this (8a) encourage us?
Hebrews 2:18; 4:14-16

(c) Meditate on these truths. Thank Christ for them. How have they encouraged your heart?

(d) How has your appreciation of Christ grown from your study?

9. Don't forget to continue memorizing Colossians 1:9-14.

Study 4 – A Worthy Walk (1:12, 13)

1. Read Colossians 1:9-14.

2. (a) What is the fourth ingredient of a worthy walk? (Verse 12a)

   (b) Why is this (2a) important to a worthy walk?

   1 Thessalonians 5:18

   Hebrews 13:15, 16

   (c) Meditate on these truths. Is this the habit pattern of your life? If not, confess it as sin to God, ask His forgiveness, and thank Him for it. Ask God to work in you that this might become more and more the habit pattern of your life.

3. (a) Why do we give thanks to the Father? (Verse 12b)

   (b) How did He do this (3a)? (Verse 13; cf. Romans 8:29, 30)

4. (a) What is the inheritance of the saints?

   Psalm 16:5, 11 (cf. Romans 8:17)

   Revelation 21:1—22:5

   (b) Why is it an inheritance in "light"?

   1 John 1:5 (cf. Revelation 21:23; 22:5)

(c) Meditate on these truths, praising and thanking God for them. What does your inheritance mean to you?

5. (a) What is the domain of darkness?

   Ephesians 6:12

   (b) What is the kingdom of the Son like?

   Revelation 1:6; 5:9, 10 (cf. Luke 1:33; John 18:36; Romans 14:17; Hebrews 12:28; James 2:5)

   (c) Have you been delivered from the domain of darkness and transferred to the kingdom of the Son?

   If yes—praise and thank God.

   If not—turn to Jesus Christ for salvation (Romans 10:9, 10; Acts 2:38)

*6. Give a summary explanation of verses 12 and 13 from what you've learned in this section.

7. (a) Review what you've learned in this section. What meant the most to you? Why? How?

   (b) Pray Colossians 1:9-13 for yourself. Pray it for your minister.

8. Keep up the good work memorizing Colossians 1:9-14.

Study 5 – *Redemption* (1:14)

1. Once again read Colossians 1:9-14.

2. What do we have in Jesus Christ? (Verse 14)

3. Define "redeem."

4. (a) Who is our redeemer? (Verse 14)
   (b) Why did we need to be redeemed?
       John 8:34 (cf. Romans 7:14)
   (c) How did Christ redeem us?
       1 Peter 1:18, 19 (cf. Matthew 20:28; Acts 20:28)
   (d) Why did Christ redeem us?
       (cf. Galatians 1:4; Titus 2:14; Revelation 5:9)
   (e) When will our redemption be complete?
       Romans 8:23 (cf. 1 Corinthians 15:50-53)

5. (a) Meditate on these truths. Praise and thank God for your redemption. Praise and thank Christ for redeeming you. If you've never accepted God's gift of redemption, do so today (Romans 10:9, 10; Acts 2:38).
   (b) Give a summary explanation of redemption from what you've learned in this section.
   (c) How has your understanding of redemption grown from your study?
   (d) What meant the most to you? Why? How?

*6. Compare what you've learned in this lesson (Studies 1-5) with what you learned about humanism in the introduction and what you see of it on TV programs and commercials.

15 and He is the image of the invisible God, the first-born of all creation.

16 For in Him all things were created, both in the heavens and on earth, visible and invisible, whether thrones or dominions or rulers or authorities—all things have been created through Him and for Him.

17 And He is before all things, and in Him all things hold together.

18 He is also head of the body, the church; and He is the beginning, the first-born from the dead; so that He Himself might come to have first place in everything.

19 For it was the Father's good pleasure for all the fulness to dwell in Him,

20 and through Him to reconcile all things to Himself, having made peace through the blood of His cross; through Him, I say, whether things on earth or things in heaven.

21 And although you were formerly alienated and hostile in mind, engaged in evil deeds,

22 yet He has now reconciled you in His fleshly body through death, in order to present you before Him holy and blameless and beyond reproach—

23 if indeed you continue in the faith firmly established and steadfast, and not moved away from the hope of the gospel that you have heard, which was proclaimed in all creation under heaven, and of which I, Paul, was made a minister

1 2 3 4 5 6 7
8 9 10 11 12

THE PREEMINENT CHRIST

Colossians 1:15-23

Most people will agree that Jesus was a good man, an exemplary one. Most believe He was a great teacher, if not the greatest. Most think His message of love and kindness was admirable. But His claim that He was God is hard to swallow; His denunciation of sin and message of judgment, unpalatable; His teaching that only through Him is there life and salvation, offensive; His right to lordship in the lives of His creation, repulsive. As long as we only place Him among the great religious teachers of history, there's no problem. But when we proclaim Him as *the* God/man, the *one* and *only* mediator between God and man, then we run into trouble.

The Colossians experienced the same difficulties. The Gnostics of their society had a whole religious system of intermediary spirits between

God and man. Each added to one's knowledge and experience of God. As long as Christians allowed Christ to take a place among these spirits, there wasn't a problem. The conflict arose when Christ was proclaimed as the only way to know God, the one full expression of God's person.

The Colossians ran the same risk of bowing to societal acceptance that we do. Paul was aware of the danger. In Colossians 1:15-23, he proclaimed Christ's uniqueness—He is the visible image of the invisible God, He is the creator, He is the head of the church, He is the one reconciler of God and men. In Him and Him alone does the fulness of God dwell. The Colossians could stand firm in these truths. So can we. So *must* we.

This is a passage to strengthen our knowledge of Christ, to open our hearts and minds to the greatness of our Savior. May you come to love, appreciate, and worship Him in a deeper way than ever before.

Study 1 – *Christ and Creation* (1:15-17)

1. Read the Introduction and Colossians 1:15-23.

2. (a) Who is Christ? (Verse 15)

   (b) What does this (2a) mean?

      John 14:9 (cf. John 1:1, 18; Hebrews 1:2, 3

   (c) Meditate on this truth. Praise Christ for who He is.

3. (a) What is Christ's relationship to creation? (Verses 16, 17)

   (b) Read the creation story in Genesis 1. Meditate on it in light of the truths you learned in 3a. Worship Christ.

   (c) In the next twenty-four hours, spend time contemplating God's creation— sun, moon, stars, plants, animals, etc., in light of Colossians 1:16, 17. Ask God to make these truths real to you as you look at His creation.

   (d) How has your understanding and/or appreciation of Christ grown from your time of meditation and contemplation?

4. (a) Who created you? (Verse 16)

   (b) Why were you created? (Verse 16b; cf. Revelation 4:11b)

   (c) Meditate on these truths.

   (d) Is this different from how you view yourself? How?

   (e) If your view of yourself (4d) is different from what you learned in 4a and 4b, confess it as sin to God, ask His forgiveness, and thank Him for it. Spend time praising and thanking God for creating you for himself. Ask that you might always live in light of this.

5. Keep on memorizing Colossians 1:9-14.

Study 2 – *Christ and the Church* (1:18)

1. Read Colossians 1:15-23 again.

2. (a) What is Christ's relationship to the church? (Verse 18a)

   (b) What do you learn about this relationship (2a) from the following Scriptures?

   Ephesians 5:23, 32

   (cf. Ephesians 4:15, 16)

   (c) Meditate on these truths. Praise and thank Christ for them.

   (d) Which truth stood out to you? Why?

3. (a) What is Christ's relationship to death? (Verse 18)

   (b) What does this (3a) mean for Him and for us?

   John 11:25, 26 (cf. 1 Corinthians 15:20-23; Hebrews 2:14, 15)

   Romans 6:10, 11 (cf. 6:4-9)

   (c) Meditate on these truths. Praise and thank God for them.

(d) How are these truths significant to your life?

4. (a) Why is Christ the creator, the head of the church, and the firstborn from the dead? (Verse 18b)

(b) Is this (4a) true in your life?
If yes—praise and thank God.
If no—confess it as sin to God, ask His forgiveness, and thank Him for it. Ask Him to work in you that this might be true in your life.

(c) If you've never received Christ as your Savior from death and the head of your life, do so today.

5. How's the memorizing coming?

Study 3 – *Christ and Reconciliation* Part 1 (1:19, 20)

1. Read Colossians 1:15-23.

2. (a) What do you learn about Christ's person in verse 19?

   (b) Why is this (2a) true? (Verse 19)

   (c) What does this (2a) mean?

      John 1:14, 16 (cf. John 17:5; Colossians 2:9; Hebrews 1:3)

   (d) Meditate on these truths. Praise and thank Christ for who He is.

3. (a) What did God do through Christ? (Verse 20a)

   (b) How did He do this (3a)? (Verse 20)

4. (a) Define reconcile.

   (b) Why does man need to be reconciled to God?

      Romans 5:12 (cf. Romans 3:23; 6:23)

   (c) When is a man reconciled to God?

      Romans 10:9, 10; Acts 2:38 (cf. 2 Corinthians 5:17-20)

(d) Why is there a need for reconciliation in nature?

Romans 8:19-22 (cf. Genesis 3:17, 18)

(e) When will nature experience the fruits of reconciliation?
Revelation 11:15 (cf. Isaiah 11:6-10)

5. Meditate on these truths. Have you been reconciled to God?

If yes—praise and thank God for your reconciliation. Ask God to give you deep appreciation of your relationship to Him.

If no—be reconciled today.

6. What ministered to you most from this section? Why?

7. Continue memorizing Colossians 1:9-14.

Study 4 – *Christ and Reconciliation,* Part 2 (1:21, 22)

1. Read Colossians 1:15-23.

2. (a) What was the Colossians (and your) condition before salvation? (Verse 21)

   (b) Why is this (2a) true of an unbeliever?

      Romans 8:5-8 (cf. Ephesians 2:1-3)

   (c) Meditate on this truth. Ask God to make it sink in.

3. (a) What did Christ do to remedy our condition? (Verse 22a)

   (b) Read the account of Christ's death in at least one of the Gospels (Matthew 26:36-46; 27:11-56; Mark 14:32-42; 15:16-41; Luke 22:39-44; 23:13-49; John 19:1-37). Ask Him to open your heart to appreciate what He went through for you.

   (c) What stands out to you from your reading?

4. (a) Why has Christ reconciled us? (Verse 22b)

   (b) When will this (4a) take place?

2 Thessalonians 1:10 (cf. Jude 24)

(c) Praise and thank Christ for this truth.

5. How has your appreciation of Christ and your salvation grown from your study?

6. Keep up the good work of memorizing Colossians 1:9-14.

Study 5 – *Continuing in the Faith* (1:23)

1. Read Colossians 1:15-23.

2. (a) What condition does Paul place on those who will be presented before Christ, holy and blameless? (Verse 23)
   (b) Why does he say this (2a)?
       Hebrews 10:38, 39 (cf. Acts 26:20)

3. (a) Why can one remain faithful to the gospel?
       Philippians 1:6 (cf. Philippians 2:13; 1 Peter 1:5)
   (b) How does one remain faithful to the gospel?
       John 15:4, 5, 10 (cf. Deuteronomy 6:5-9; Psalm 119:4)
       2 Peter 1:10 (cf. 1:5-9; Hebrews 6:11, 12)

4. (a) Meditate on these truths, asking God for understanding.
   (b) How has your understanding of salvation grown from your study?
   (c) Are there any steps (question 3b) you need to take to remain faithful to the gospel? Ask God for insight.

*5. Compare what you've learned about salvation in this study with James 2:14-26.

6. How's your memorization coming?

*7. Compare what you've learned in this lesson (Studies 1 -5) with what you learned about humanism in the introduction to the first lesson, and what you see and hear of it in music, TV, and movies.

24 Now I rejoice in my sufferings for your sake, and in my flesh I do my share on behalf of His body (which is the church) in filling up that which is lacking in Christ's afflictions.

25 Of this church I was made a minister according to the stewardship from God bestowed on me for your benefit, that I might fully carry out the preaching of the word of God,

26 that is, the mystery which has been hidden from the past ages and generations; but has now been manifested to His saints,

27 to whom God willed to make known what is the riches of the glory of this mystery among the Gentiles, which is Christ in you, the hope of glory.

28 And we proclaim Him, admonishing every man and teaching every man with all wisdom, that we may present every man complete in Christ.

29 And for this purpose also I labor, striving according to His power, which mightily works within me.

1 For I want you to know how great a struggle I have on your behalf, and for those who are at Laodicea, and for all those who have not personally seen my face,

2 that their hearts may be encouraged, having been knit together in love, and attaining to all the wealth that comes from the full assurance of understanding, resulting in a true knowledge of God's mystery, that is, Christ Himeself,

3 in whom are hidden all the treasures of wisdom and knowledge.

4 I say this in order that no one may delude you with persuasive argument.

5 For even though I am absent in body, nevertheless I am with you in spirit, rejoicing to see your good discipline and the stability of your faith in Christ.

6 As you therefore have received Christ Jesus the Lord, so walk in Him,

7 having been firmly rooted and now being built up in Him and established in your faith, just as you were instructed, and overflowing with gratitude.

1 2 3 4 5 6 7
8 9 10 11 12

THE GLORIOUS MYSTERY

Colossians 1:24—2:7

Mysteries are intriguing. They capture our curiosity and tax our ingenuity. Whether we play a game, read a book, or watch a surprise thriller, we must step by step put together the clues to figure out "who done it."

You may be surprised to know that the Bible is a "mystery" book—not a "who done it," but a revelation of something hidden. (That's the Biblical definition of a mystery.) In Colossians 1:27, Paul tells us about a glorious mystery—one which had been hidden from the Old Testament people but now was clearly laid out for the New Testament church. It is the very heart of our existence as new creatures in Christ. It may seem simple, it may be very familiar, but it's only as we begin to live experientially in the reality of this mystery that we experience the deep joy and power of the Christian life.

Paul does not just state the fact of this glorious mystery. He goes on to give us instruction as to how we can live in light of this powerful truth. Ask God to encourage and to empower you as you uncover the truth of His glorious mystery and learn how to walk in light of it.

Study 1 – *The Minister and the Mystery* (1:24-27)

1. Read the introduction and Colossians 1:24-2:7.

2. (a) How did Paul view his sufferings? (Verse 24)

   *(b) What insights into what Paul is saying in verse 24 do you gain from 2 Corinthians 4:7-12?

   (c) Meditate on what you've learned, asking God for insight on how do these truths need to affect your thinking and living.

3. Why was Paul a minister? (Verse 25)

4. The word "mystery" in the New Testament means "something not before revealed." It is something that cannot be known without divine revelation.

5. (a) Why didn't all the past generations before Christ came know this mystery? (Verse 26)

   (b) Who are the ones who now know the mystery? (Verse 26)

   (c) Why can they know it? (Verse 27)

6. (a) What is the mystery? (Verse 27)

   (b) What further understanding of this mystery do the following verses give you? John 14:16-20 (cf. 1 Corinthians 3:16); Romans 8:10; Galatians 2:20

   (c) Meditate on this truth. Ask God to make it real to you. Praise and thank God for this truth.

   (d) How does this truth affect how you view yourself (self-image)?

7. (a) Why is this mystery rich in glory?

   (Romans 9:23)

   (b) Meditate on this. Praise and thank God for His love toward you.

8. What is the glory we hope for because of this mystery?

   Romans 8:18, 23-25, (cf. 1 Peter 1:3, 4)

9. Review what you've learned about the mystery. What meant the most to you? Why? How?

10. Continue memorizing and reviewing Colossians 1:9-14.

Study 2 – *Teaching and Admonishing* (1:28, 29)

1. Read Colossians 1:24—2:7.

2. (a) What was Paul's purpose in proclaiming Christ? (Verse 28b)
   (b) What did he do to accomplish this purpose? (Verses 28 and 29)

3. In the following verses note how Paul combines teaching and admonishing.

Teaching About Christ's Person and Work

   (a) Romans 15:2, 3

   (b) Ephesians 5:2

   (c) Philippians 2:3-8

   (d) Colossians 3:13

Reference	*Admonition*
(a)	(a)
(b)	(b)
(c)	(c)
(d)	(d)

4. Review your chart. What stands out to you how Paul combined teaching and admonishing?

*5. (a) Why is it important to link all exhortation to teaching about Christ? (Hint: Remember what you learned in Study 1, question 6.)

(b) Why do you need both teaching and admonishing to become complete (mature) in Christ? (Back up your answer with Scripture if you can.)

6. Are you enjoying your memorizing of Colossians 1:9-14?

Study 3 – *Encouraged Hearts* (2:1-3)

1. Read Colossians 1:24—2:7.

2. (a) What was Paul's overriding concern for Christians he'd never met personally? (Verses 1, 2a)

   (b) How does this (2a) happen? (Verse 2b)

   (c) What is the result? (Verse 2c)

3. (a) Share a time when you were encouraged through the love of a brother or sister in Christ.

   (b) Thank God for what you wrote down in 3a. Write a note of thanks and appreciation to that person, sharing with them what an encouragement they were to you.

   (c) Express love to someone today to encourage them.

4. (a) What is the "full assurance of understanding" that Paul is referring to?

   Colossians 1:27, (Study 1, questions 6-8)

(b) What is the "wealth" in our lives when we stand fully assured in this truth and know it experientially?

John 14:27 (cf. John 16:33)

1 Corinthians 1:30

2 Timothy 1:7 (cf. John 8:32)

(c) Meditate on the things you've learned. Praise and thank God for them. Ask God that you might experience fully these truths.

(d) What especially encouraged you from these truths?

*5. (a) What are hidden in Christ? (Verse 3)

(b) How do you discover something that is hidden?

(c) How do you discover what is hidden in Christ?

John 5:39 (cf Proverbs 2:1-8)

6. Memorize and review Colossians 1:9-14.

Study 4 – *Discipline and Stability* (2:4, 5)

1. Read Colossians 1:24-2:7.

2. Why was Paul sharing these truths about Christ in his letter to the Colossians? (Verse 4)

3. What two things in the Colossians' lives did Paul rejoice over? (Verse 5)

4. (a) Define discipline.

   (b) Why is discipline important in our walk with Christ?
   1 Timothy 4:7,8 (cf. 1 Corinthians 9:24-27)

5. How does one maintain stability in their faith?

   Psalm 78:8
   Hebrews 3:13
   1 Peter 5:6-10

6. (a) Meditate on these truths. What stands out to you? Why?

   (b) Asking God for insight, how do you need to apply these truths in your life?

*7. What relationship is there between discipline and stability in our walk with God?

8. How's the memorizing coming?

Study 5 – *Walking in Him* (2:6, 7)

1. Read Colossians 1:24—2:7.

2. (a) How were the Colossians to walk with Christ? (Verse 6)

   (b) What is the essence of this walk?

   2 Corinthians 5:7 (cf. Ephesians 2:8, 9)

   (c) In what does this walk consist?
   Colossians 2:7

3. How is one "firmly rooted" in Christ?

   Psalm 1:1-3

   Jeremiah 17:7, 8

4. How are we "built up" in Him?

   Matthew 7:24, 25

5. How are we "established" in our faith?

   2 Chronicles 20:20

   2 Corinthians 1:21 (cf. 1 Peter 5:10; Jude 24; 2 Chronicles 20:20)

6. What do you learn about the importance of "gratitude" from Luke 17:11-19?

7. (a) Meditate on these truths. Are they true of your life? How or how not?

   (b) Praise and thank God for the ways your life does reflect these truths. Confess as sin to God the ways in which your life does not reflect these truths. Ask His forgiveness, and thank Him for it. Ask Him to work in your life in these areas. Thank Him for what He's going to do (Ephesians 3:20).

8. How has your appreciation and/or understanding of the Christian life grown from your study of this section?

9. Can you say Colossians 1:9-14 yet?

*10. What insights do you gain into the interrelationship between members of the body of Christ from Colossians 1:24—2:7?

*11. (a) How could the things you've learned in Colossians 1:24—2:7 help you stand strong against the humanism which pervades the world around you?

    (b) How could you help your children with these truths so they, too, stand strong against the humanistic philosophy they face daily in television, school, music, etc.?

8 See to it that no one takes you captive through philosophy and empty deception, according to the tradition of men, according to the elementary principles of the world, rather than according to Christ.

9 For in Him all the fulness of Deity dwells in bodily form,

10 and in Him you have been made complete, and He is the head over all rule and authority;

11 and in Him you were also circumcised with a circumcision made without hands, in the removal of the body of the flesh by the circumcision of Christ;

12 having been buried with Him in baptism, in which you were also raised up with Him through faith in the working of God, who raised Him from the dead.

13 And when you were dead in your transgressions and the uncircumcision of your flesh, He made you alive together with Him, having forgiven us all our transgressions,

14 having cancelled out the certificate of debt consisting of decrees against us and which was hostile to us; and He has taken it out of the way, having nailed it to the cross.

15 When He had disarmed the rulers and authorities, He made a public display of them, having triumphed over them through Him.

1 2 3 4 5 6 7 8 9 10 11 12

WHOSE CAPTIVE ARE YOU?

Colossians 2:8-15

CAPTURED! HELD HOSTAGE! The words scream from headlines and become "top stories" on the evening news. We all feel the pain when a fellow citizen endures such indignity and suffering. We closely follow their ordeal, agonizing with their families, and then celebrating when liberation finally comes.

As citizens of heaven (Philippians 3:20), every new creature in Christ runs the risk of being captured, of becoming a hostage. There is a world philosophy which is not only diametrically opposed to who we are in Christ, but will make us its prisoner if we do not take care to withstand its influence.

In Colossians 2:8-15, Paul addresses this problem. He warns us of the danger and reminds us of our Lord and King. This is family truth, truth directed to those who have been born into God's family through repentance of sin and confession of Christ as Savior and Lord. We are not to succumb to the philosophy of the world, because we belong to Christ. He is deserving of our total obedience and allegiance because of who He is and what He's done in making us His own. When these truths sink into our minds and hearts, they are powerful incentives to live as Christ's captive rather than the world's. May you be strengthened in your obedience and allegiance to Christ as you study.

Study 1 – *Worldly Philosophy* (2:8)

1. Read the introduction and Colossians 2:8-15.

2. What is the danger we face as new creatures in Christ? (Verse 8)

3. (a) What is the basis of the philosophy of the world?

    1 John 2:16

   (b) Do one or more of the following: (1) Watch a TV program and commercials. (2) Listen to a secular song. (3) Read a secular magazine article or chapter from a secular book. (4) Then write down everything you notice in these that is based in the world's philosophy (3a).

4. What is the philosophy (teaching) of Christ for daily living?
   Luke 9:23-25 (cf. John 12:24-26)

5. (a) What does the world think of Christ's directives for living?

    1 Corinthians 1:18

   (b) What does God think of the world's philosophy?

1 Corinthians 3:19

6. (a) Meditate on what you've learned. Evaluate your thinking and living in light of
these truths. Write it down. Be honest
with yourself. Ask God to open your
eyes to which philosophy dominates
your thinking and living.

   (b) Where your thinking and living is dominated by worldly philosophy, confess it
as sin to God, ask His forgiveness, and
thank Him for it.

7. (a) Why is it so important to not be taken
captive by the philosophy of the world?

   James 4:4 (cf. 4:1-5; John 2:15, 17)

   (b) How do we keep from being conformed
to the world?

   Romans 12:2

8. (a) How much time do you spend feeding
your mind and life with God's perspec-
tive? (Reading, studying, memorizing
the Bible, meditating on Scripture,
prayer, etc. The following can also be
helpful *if* used in *addition* to the time in
the Bible and *evaluated* in the light of
Scripture—Christian radio and T.V.,
Christian books and periodicals, church
services and Bible study groups,

Christian music, Scripture centered conversations.)

(b) How much time do you spend feeding your mind and life with worldly philosophy. (Watching T.V., listening to music, reading books or magazines, going to movies, conversations, etc.)

(c) What correlation is there between what you feed your mind and life (8a and 8b) and your evaluation of yourself in 6a?

(d) What steps do you need to take to bring your thinking and living in line with God's truth? (Ask God for insight.)

9. Review Colossians 1:9-14.

Study 2 – *Reasons for Allegiance,* Part 1 (2:9, 10)

1. Read Colossians 2:8-15.

2. Having stated the importance of following Christ rather than worldly wisdom in verse 8, Paul explains in verses 9-15 why Christ is deserving of our total obedience and allegiance.

3. (a) What is the first reason Paul gives for total obedience and allegiance to Christ? (Verse 9)

    (b) What does this (3a) mean?

    Matthew 1:23 (cf. Luke 3:22; Titus 2:13)

    (c) Meditate on these truths. Though these truths may be familiar, ask God to deepen your appreciation of them, really make them sink down deep. Praise Christ for who He is.

4. (a) What is the second reason we as new creatures in Christ are to obey and fully follow Christ? (Verse 10a)

    (b) What does this (4a) mean?

    Galatians 3:26, 27 (especially 27b)

    (c) Meditate on this truth—especially in light of what you learned in question 3.

Ask God to put this truth deep down into your heart and thinking. Praise and thank God for this glorious truth.

(d) What does this truth tell you about how God feels about you? (Back up your answer with Scripture. Luke 3:22 can get you started.)

(e) Spend time basking in the truth of 4d. Ask God to make it real to your mind and emotions. Soak in His love toward you.

5. (a) What is the third reason Paul gives for obedience to Christ? (Verse 10b)

(b) What does this (5a) mean?

1 Peter 3:22 (cf. Ephesians 1:22)

(c) Meditate on this truth. Praise Christ for His exalted position.

6. (a) How has your appreciation of Christ grown from your study?

(b) How could remembering these truths help you in your obedience and allegiance to Christ?

7. Continue reviewing Colossians 1:9-14.

Study 3 – *Reasons for Allegiance,* Part 2 (2:11, 12)

1. Read Colossians 2:8-15.

2. What is the fourth reason Paul gives for total obedience and allegiance to Christ? (Verse 11)

3. The "body of the flesh" is our physical body (our humanness) which is dominated by sin (Romans 7:14b, 23b). Every new creature in Christ experienced at his new birth a spiritual circumcision, a release from the power of the flesh to dominate the life. (It is important to distinguish between the "old man" of Scripture and the "body of the flesh." The "old man" is the person we were in Adam (Romans 5:12-19). That person died in our identification with Christ in His crucifixion (Romans 6:6). We were then raised with Him. We are now new creatures in Christ, a new righteous person indwelt by the Spirit of God (Romans 6:5; 2 Corinthians 5:17; Romans 8:9, 10). Because of this, our fleshly bodies, with all impulses and habit patterns of sin etched in our brains, no longer have the right to dominate our lives (Romans 6:6). Though we experience the conflict of flesh versus spirit and long for our final redemption—a new body with no more conflict (Romans 6:7; 8:23)—we now can rejoice in who we are in Him and experience His power in daily living.)

4. Why was it necessary that we be released from the dominance of the flesh?
(Romans 8:5-8; (especially verse 8)

5. (a) How were we released?
Colossians 2:12; Romans 6:3-7

(b) What is the result in our lives because of this (5a)?

Romans 6:4b
Romans 6:6b-7
Romans 8:1
Romans 8:2
Romans 8:10

(c) What must we do to experience these truths in our daily living?

Romans 6:11 (cf. 6:8-10)

Romans 6:12, 13

6. (a) Meditate on what you've learned. Praise and thank God for these truths. What stands out to you?

(b) How do you need to live in light of these truths? (Ask God for insight.)

(If you would like further study in this area, there are several good books out. *Birthright! Christian, Do You Know Who You Are?* by David Needham; *Handbook to Happiness* by Charles R. Solomon.)

Study 4 – *Reasons for Allegiance*, Part 3 (2:13-14)

1. Read Colossians 2:8-15 again.

2. What is the fifth reason we are to be obedient to Christ and follow Him fully? (Verse 13)

3. (a) What were we like when we were dead in our transgressions?

   Ephesians 2:1-3

   (b) What prompted God to make us alive together with himself?

   Ephesians 2:4, 5

   (c) What is the result for us?

   Ephesians 2:6, 7

   (d) Meditate on these truths. Praise and thank God for His heart toward you.

4. (a) Why can we experience life with God? (Verse 13b)

   (b) Why could He do this (4a)? (Verse 14)

5. (a) What is the "certificate of debt consisting of decrees against us"?

   Galatians 3:10

(b) Why was it hostile to us?
Romans 3:19, 20 (cf. Galatians 3:10)

(c) How was it cancelled?
Colossians 2:14b (cf. Galatians 3:13)

6. (a) Meditate on these truths. Praise and thank God for what He's done for you. If you've never accepted God's gift of life and forgiveness, do so today.

(b) How has your appreciation and/or understanding of your salvation grown from your study of this section?

7. Review and meditate on Colossians 1:9-14.

Study 5 – *Truth to Stand On* (2:15)

1. Read Colossians 2:8-15.

2. What truth do we need to know to stand firm in our allegiance to Christ? (Verse 15)

3. (a) Who are the rulers and authorities?

    Ephesians 6:11, 12

   (b) How do they try to keep us from total obedience and allegiance to Christ?

    Revelation 12:10 (cf. Zechariah 3:1)

    Job 1:8-12 (especially verse 12;) (cf. Job 2:1-7)

    John 8:44 (cf. 2 Corinthians 11:13-15)

   (c) In the face of this (3b), how do we live in light of Colossians 2:15?
    Ephesians 6:10-18

   *(d) Why can Colossians 2:15 be such an encouragement to us in the face of attacks?

    Romans 8:31-39

4. (a) Review the truths you've learned. Praise and thank God for His triumphant power. Ask Him to imprint these truths

deep in your heart and life that you might live in their strength and comfort.

(b) Which truth that you learned in this section do you particularly need to remember to stand firm in your obedience and allegiance to Christ? Why?

(c) How have these truths deepened your understanding of the Christian life?

(d) What encouraged you most from what you learned in this section?

5. Congratulations, you did it. Say Colossians 1:9-14 to someone today.

*6. How has this lesson (Studies 1-5) encouraged you in your obedience and allegiance to Christ?

*7. From what you've learned in this lesson, how is Christ central to the Christian life?

16 Therefore let no one act as your judge in regard to food or drink or in respect to a festival or a new moon or a Sabbath day—

17 things which are a mere shadow of what is to come; but the substance belongs to Christ.

18 Let no one keep defrauding you of your prize by delighting in self-abasement and the worship of the angels, taking his stand on visions he has seen, inflated without cause by his fleshly mind,

19 and not holding fast to the head, from whom the entire body, being supplied and held together by the joints and ligaments, grows with a growth which is from God.

20 If you have died with Christ to the elementary principles of the world, why, as if you were living in the world, do you submit yourself to decrees, such as,

21 "Do not handle, do not taste, do not touch!"

22 (which all refer to things destined to perish with the using)—in accordance with the commandments and teachings of men?

23 These are matters which have, to be sure, the appearance of wisdom in self-made religion and self-abasement and severe treatment of the body, but are of no value against fleshly indulgence.

1 If then you have been raised up with Christ, keep seeking the things above, where Christ is, seated at the right hand of God.

2 Set your mind on the things above, not on the things that are on earth.

3 For you have died and your life is hidden with Christ in God.

4 When Christ, who is our life, is revealed, then you also will be revealed with Him in glory.

1 2 3 4 5 6 7 8 9 10 11 12

TRUE SPIRITUALITY, Part 1

"The Foundation"

Colossians 2:16—3:4

The strength of a building is determined by its foundation. Unless a deep, solid foundation is laid, the structure will never withstand the stress it must face. A building is only as good as its foundation.

The quality of our walk with God is the same. The foundation is all important. Unless the foundation is understood, the building of our spiritual lives will be weak and ineffective.

The foundation of our Christian living is stated in Colossians 2:11, 12. It is our death and resurrection in Jesus Christ. That is the foundation stone of all our living as new creatures in Christ. It is the foundation of true spirituality.

Having mentioned the doctrinal truth of our death and resurrection with Christ in Colossians 2:11, 12, Paul goes on in 2:16-3:4 to explain how it is the key truth, the foundational truth to

73

Christian living. It means that no external observances make for true spirituality. We have died to those things and to any fleshly effort or indulgence. Our spirituality rests in our identity in Christ since we have been raised up with Him in spirit.

A true understanding of our new identity in Christ is crucial to a solid foundation for our spiritual lives. This truth must sink down deep into our hearts and minds if we are to experience true spirituality. The Christian life is not the performance of externals but the reality of a new life within, a new identity.

In the rest of chapter 3 we'll discover what affect this new identity has in our daily living. But first we need to dig deeply into the foundational truth and set our hearts and minds on "Christ, who is our life."

May God open wide the eyes of your heart to understand and appreciate who you are in Him.

If you have never received Jesus Christ as your Savior and your Lord, then there is no way to experience true spirituality. Accept Him today. Then you, too, can enjoy a new identity and life in Him.

Study 1 – *Pressure From Judaism* (2:16-17)

1. Read the introduction (Underline what stands out to you.) and Colossians 2:16—3:4.

2. (a) What were those loyal to Judaism judging the Colossians about? (Verse 16)

   (b) Why were these things (verse 16) not vital to their Christian lives? (Verse 17)

3.*(a) What are these regulations stated in verse 16?

   Deuteronomy 14:3 (cf. 14:4-21)

   Leviticus 10:9 (cf. Numbers 6:2, 3)

   Exodus 23:14-17 (cf. 23:15-17)

   Leviticus 23:3 (cf. 23:23-36)

   (b) What does the New Testament tell us about these regulations?

   Hebrews 9:8-10; 10:1

   (c) What does the Scripture tell us about Christ?

   Hebrews 10:9-14

(d) Give a summary explanation of why the Colossian Christians did not have to follow Judaistic rituals.

4. Meditate on the truths you've learned. Praise and thank Christ for the perfect salvation you have in Him. Thank Him for your deliverance from the law.

5. (a) Are there any observances or external regulations that you are counting on for acceptance or good standing with God?

(b) What do the Scriptures you've studied tell you about them?

(c) If you've never accepted God's gift of salvation in Christ, accept it today.

(d) If you're a new creature in Christ and still trusting in regulations for good standing with God, how do you need to apply these truths to your thinking?

6. What do the truths you've studied mean to you?

7. Begin memorizing Colossians 3:1-4. (You have two weeks to do it.)

Study 2 – *Pressure From Ecstatics and Ascetics* (2:18-23)

1. Read Colossians 2:16—3:4.

2. (a) What did ecstatics base their spirituality and authority on? (Verse 18)

   (b) What is Paul's assessment of them? (Verse 18)

   (c) In contrast, what is essential for spiritual growth for the church? (Verse 19)

   (d) What further understanding of this truth do you gain from Ephesians 4:11-16? (cf. Colossians 3:16)

3. (a) Review what you've learned. Evaluate your minister, your church, and radio and T.V. preachers in light of these truths. (Write down your evaluations.) This is not being critical of any of these peoples. It is examining to see if they are in line with Scripture.

   (b) Evaluate your own life in light of these truths. (Write it down.)

   (c) Where you fall short, ask God to work in you. Where your life reflects these truths, praise and thank Him for His work in you.

(d) Pray for your church and minister in light of these truths.

4. (a) What did the ascetics say was necessary for spirituality? (Verses 20-22; cf. 1 Timothy 4:3)

   (b) How do these things (4a) appear? (Verse 23)

   ·(c) What is God's estimate of them? (Verse 23b)

   (d) What is "fleshly indulgence"?

   Galatians 5:19-21, 24 (cf. 1 Peter 4:3)

   (e) What is our only victory over the flesh? (Verse 20a; cf. Romans 6:10, 11; Lesson 5, Study 3)

   (f) Review these truths (4a-e). Praise and thank God for your victory over the flesh in Christ.

   (g) How have you tried to live in victory over the flesh?

   (h) How do you need to apply these truths to your life?

   (i) Summarize these truths in your own words.

5. Continue memorizing Colossians 3:1-4

Study 3 – *Seeking and Setting* (3:1, 2)

1. Read Colossians 2:16—3:4.

2. How are we to live in light of our spiritual resurrection with Christ? (Verse 1)

3. (a) Define seek.

   (b) What are the "things above" we are to seek?

   Psalm 17:15 (cf. Psalm 73:25; Matthew 6:33)

   Psalm 119:89

   Ephesians 1:3 (cf. Galatians 5:22, 23; James 3:17)

   (c) How does one do this kind of seeking? (Verse 2)

   (d) Why are we to set our minds on things above?

   Matthew 6:19-21; (cf. Luke 12:15)

   2 Corinthians 4:18 (cf. 1 John 2:17)

   Philippians 3:20

(e) What is involved in setting our minds on things above? Psalm 1:2 (cf. Psalm 119: 11, 97 Deuteronomy 6:6-9)

4. (a) Meditate on what you've learned. What stood out to you most? Why?

(b) Asking God for insight, how do these truths need to affect your life?

*5. Give a summary explanation of the "how, what, and why" of seeking and setting our minds on things above.

6. Keep working on memorizing Colossians 3:1-4.

Study 4 – *Identity in Christ* (3:3, 4a)

1. Read Colossians 2:16—3:4.

2. (a) What is your identity as a new creature in Christ? (Verse 3, 4a)

    (b) Meditate on this truth. Praise and thank God for it.

    (c) How is this (2a) different from how you view yourself?

    (d) Ask God to renew your mind and emotions in this truth.

3. (a) When did your identity in Christ take place in the heart of God?

    Ephesians 1:4 (cf. 2 Timothy 1:9)

    (b) Why did it take place in the heart of God?

    Jeremiah 31:3 (cf. John 17:23b, 24b)

    (c) How do we enter into the experience of it from God's side?

    John 6:44 (cf. John 17:6)

(d) What happens to us?

  2 Corinthians 5:17 (cf. John 3:5; Romans 6:4, 5)

(e) How do we enter into the experience of it from our side?
  Romans 10:9, 10; Acts 2:38
  (cf. John 1:12; Ephesians 2:8, 9)

(f) What is our assurance?

  John 10:28, 29 (cf. Romans 8:16)

(g) What is the result in our living?

  Galatians 2:20 (cf. Ephesians 2:10)

(h) Meditate on these truths. Praise and thank God for them. Ask Him to sink them deep into your heart.

(i) If you've never received Christ, do so to-day.

4. (a) What ministered to you most from this section? Why? How?

  *(b) Give a summary explanation of salvation from what you've learned in this section.

5. Continue memorizing Colossians 3:1-4.

Study 5 – *The Revelation of Christ and Christians* (3:4)

1. Read Colossians 2:16—3:4.

2. (a) When will our true identity in Christ be fully revealed? (Verse 4)

    (b) When is Christ going to be revealed?

        1 Thessalonians 5:1, 2

    (c) How is Christ going to be revealed?
         Luke 21:27 (cf. Matthew 25:31;
         Revelation 19:11-16)

    (d) What is His purpose in coming?

        2 Thessalonians 1:10

        Matthew 16:27

    (e) What will we be like?

        1 John 3:2 (cf. Philippians 3:21)

    (f) What will we experience?

        Romans 8:18

        Ephesians 2:7

3. Meditate on these truths. Praise and thank God for them. What do they mean to you? Why?

4. How's your memorizing of Colossians 3:1-4 coming?

*5. How has your understanding and/or appreciation of your identity in Christ grown from this lesson (Studies 1-5)?

5 Therefore consider the members of your earthly body as dead to immorality, impurity, passion, evil desire, and greed, which amounts to idolatry.

6 For it is on account of these things that the wrath of God will come,

7 and in them you also once walked, when you were living in them.

8 But now you also, put them all aside; angner, wrath, malice, slander, and abusive speech from your mouth.

9 Do not lie to one another, since you laid aside the old self with its evil practices.

10 and have put on the new self who is being renewed to a true knowledge according to the image of the One who created him,

11 —a renewal in which there is no distinction between Greek and Jew, circumcised and uncircumcised, barbarian, Scythian, slave and freeman, but Christ is all, and in all.

TRUE SPIRITUALITY, Part 2

"Putting Off the Old"

Colossians 3:5-11

Death is not a pleasant subject. In fact, we live in a society that attempts to deny it at all costs. But as new creatures in Christ, we have *already* experienced a *glorious* death—a death to sin and the rule of the flesh. We have died with Christ to *all* that sin encompasses. This is fact. This is foundational truth.

God desires that each one of us live daily in the full experience of this wonderful truth, for it produces holiness of life and tremendous freedom. But it is a painful process. The death we died with Christ in spirit must become a reality in the practical living of our lives. Death is painful, death is stripping, death rips at the core of our beings. But death to sin and the flesh is worth all the agony.

God allows various circumstances in our lives to let the sinful passions and habit patterns which have made up our living to be brought to light.

These things have been so much a part of us that they often seem like they *are* us. But that's where we have to remember the foundational truth of our identity in Christ. We have died to those sinful passions, habits, and fleshly living. As they come to light, we die to them in experience. We must count the truth of our death and resurrection to be true and say no in the power of Christ's life within. We must live like who we really are—a new creature in Christ.

This is a process, not a once for all experience. The habit patterns etched in our brains are strong. But as time after time we renew our minds in the truth and act accordingly, a new habit pattern is set. In the process, we must remember that emotions are only that, emotions. They are not necessarily truth. They are not us. They are feelings. We may need to pour them out to God, but we must stand firm in the truth even in the face of roaring emotions.

This process of living doesn't happen by self-effort, but by moment by moment turning to Christ and trusting His power within. We give up the fight in any fleshly strength and count on Him, apart from whom we can do nothing (John 15:5).

In Colossians 3:5-11, we learn some of the sinful passions and habits to which we are dead. This is serious business. God's wrath and judgment are coming because of sin. How important that we view sin as He does and live in light of our death to sin.

God can strengthen your heart to face death to sin and the flesh. And may He renew you to the true image of who you are in Christ. The joy of holiness awaits you.

Study 1 – *Dead to Sin* (3:5)

1. Read the introduction (Underline what stands out to you.) and Colossians 3:5-11.

2. How is the fact of your death and resurrection with Christ to affect your conduct? (Verse 5 cf. Galatians 2:20; Romans 6:8-11)

3. Read carefully the following definitions, underlining what stands out to you.

   (a) immorality—*any* sex outside of marriage. It is an action.

   (b) impurity—moral uncleanness. Refers to one's thoughts, intentions, and actions. Sensual, lustful living.

   (c) passion—extreme, compelling emotion. Recklessly extravagant, extremely wasteful (Examples—anger, rage, lust).

   (d) evil desire—wicked cravings—morally or ethically evil. All manner of lusts and destructive desires.

   (e) greed—Self seeking. A desire to have more (especially what others have); material possessions or sensual pleasures.

   (f) idolatry—worship of false gods. Setting the mind and emotions on things other than God.

4. (a) What does the Scripture tell us about these things?

   Exodus 20:4-6

   Proverbs 14:30 (cf. James 1:14, 15)

   1 Corinthians 6:18-20 (cf. Matthew 5:27, 28)

   Ephesians 5:3, 11, 12 (cf.
   1 Thessalonians 4:3-8; 1 Timothy 6:9, 10)

   (b) Meditate on what you've learned. What stands out to you about what God has to say about these things? Why?

   (c) If you have been disobedient in any of these things, confess it as sin to God, ask His forgiveness, and thank Him for it.

   (d) If you've sinned against anyone in this area, go to them confessing your sin and ask their forgiveness.

   (e) Asking God for insight, what steps do you need to take to be obedient in the areas where you've been disobedient?

5. Continue memorizing and reviewing Colossians 3:1-4.

Study 2 – *God's Wrath* (3:6)

1. Again read Colossians 3:5-11.

2. Why is the wrath of God going to come? (Verse 6; cf. verse 5)

3. (a) Define wrath.

   (b) What goes hand in hand with God's wrath?

   Romans 2:5

4. (a) What do you learn about God's wrath and coming judgment from the following verses?

   Isaiah 13:6-13 (cf. 2 Peter 3:10-13)

   John 3:36 (cf. 1 Thessalonians 1:9, 10)

   2 Thessalonians 1:7-9 (cf. Revelation 20:11-15)

   *(b) For further knowledge and understanding of God's wrath and judgment, read the following passages from Revelation. Jot down what stands out to you.
   Revelation 6:12-17; 8:1, 2, 7—9:21; 11:15-19; 14:9-11; 15:1, 5—16:21; 19:11-21

5. (a) Meditate on what you have learned. Praise God for His wrath and judgment

91

of sin.

(b) What stands out to you about God's wrath and coming judgment?

(c) How has your view of God grown from your study?

6. (a) In light of how God views the things listed in verse 5, what should your attitude be toward them?

(b) Ask God to work in your heart to help you view sin as He does.

(c) List the TV programs you watch. Write down for each one how many of the things listed in Colossians 3:5 are an integral part of the program. Review your list.

(d) In light of what you learned in Study 1 and in this study, what changes need to be made in your television viewing habits?

*(e) Evaluate your movie watching, reading, and music listening in the same way.

(f) Ask God to strengthen you that you might glorify Him in your entertainment.

7. Keep on memorizing and reviewing Colossians 3:1-4.

Study 3 – *Put Away* ... (3:8, 9a)

1. Read Colossians 3:5-11.

2. How is our new life in Christ to further affect our living? (Verses 8, 9a)

3. (a) anger—an abiding, settled condition of the mind. A habitual anger with desires for revenge.

   (b) wrath—a sudden, violent outburst of anger. Agitated feelings.

   (c) malice—vicious ill will. A desire to injure.

   (d) slander—speech that injures a person's character or reputation. Scornful language directed against someone.

   (e) abusive speech—base, shameful, obscene speech.

   (f) lying—any falsehood or deception. To give a false impression.

4. (a) What do you learn about these things from the following verses?

   Proverbs 10:18

Proverbs 16:32; (cf.29:22; Ecclesiastes 7:9; Ephesians 4:26, 27; 2 Timothy 2:24; James 1:19, 20)

Ephesians 4:25 (cf. John 8:44)

Ephesians 4:29 (cf. Ephesians 5:4)

(b) Meditate on what you've learned. Ask God to convict you of any sin in your life in these areas. If He does, confess it as sin to Him, ask His forgiveness, and thank, Him for it.

(c) Asking God for insight, what steps do you need to take to put away from your life the things He convicted you of?

(d) If you've sinned against anyone in any of these areas, go to them. Confess your sin and ask their forgiveness. (Ask God for wisdom about *when* to go.)

(e) What stood out to you from what you learned in this study? Why?

5. How's your memorizing and reviewing of Colossians 3:1-4 coming?

Study 4 – *The Basis of Obedience* (3:7, 9b, 10)

1. Read Colossians 3:5-11.

2. (a) In Study 1 and Study 3 (verses 5, 8, 9a) we learned about things which are not to be part of our lives as new creatures in Christ. Why do we need this kind of exhortation? (Verse 7)

   (b) Why are they no longer to be a part of our lives? (Verses 9b, 10a)

   (c) What is true of us as new creatures in Christ? (Verse 10)

   (d) What do you learn about this (2c) from the following Scriptures?
   2 Corinthians 3:18 (cf. Romans 8:29)
   2 Corinthians 4:16
   Philippians 2:13
   2 Peter 1:3

   *(e) Give a summary explanation of Colossians 3:7, 9b, 10.

3. (a) Meditate on what you've learned. Praise and thank God for these truths. What ministered to you most? Why? How?

   (b) How can the truths you've learned in this section strengthen you in your obedience to the exhortations in verses 5, 8, 9a?

*4. Explain Colossians 3:5-10 in light of Romans 6:1-13 (cf. Lesson 5, Study 3).

5. Continue memorizing and reviewing Colossians 3:1-4.

Study 5 – *No Distinctions* (3:11)

1. Read Colossians 3:5-11.

2. What is true of all new creatures in Christ? (Verse 11)

3. (a) Before the birth of the church, what had been the distinctions between Jews and non-Jews?
   Ephesians 2:11, 12 (cf. Romans 9:4, 5)

   (b) What was their relationship to one another like?
   Acts 10:28

   (c) How did that change?
   Ephesians 2:13, 14

   (d) What is the result? (Verse 11; cf. Acts 10:34, 35)

   (e) What does it mean that Christ is all and in all?
   Colossians 1:27 (cf. Romans 11:36)

4. (a) In verse 11, Paul mentions other distinctions people draw between themselves and others. Cultural ones—barbarians, Scythians: those considered less "cultured" than ourselves. Social ones—slave and free; economic and social "barriers" we put up. What does verse 11 tell you about any such distinctions we might make?

(b) What further understanding of this truth do you gain from James 2:1-9?

(c) Are there any distinctions you draw between yourself and others in the body of Christ? How?

(d) Confess as sin to God anything you wrote down in 4c, ask His forgiveness, and thank Him for it. If you've sinned against someone in this way, go to them and ask their forgiveness.

(e) Asking God for insight, what steps do you need to take to live in light of these truths?

5. (a) Meditate on what you've learned. Praise and thank God for the oneness you have with your brothers and sisters in Christ. Praise Christ, your all in all.

(b) How has your understanding of the church grown from your study of this section?

(c) How has your appreciation of Christ grown from your study of this section?

6. Do you have Colossians 3:1-4 memorized?

*7. Compare what you've learned in Colossians 3:5-11 with humanism.

*8. How can you help your children with these truths in light of the humanism that bombards them?

12 And so, as those who have been chosen of God, holy and beloved, put on a heart of compassion, kindness, humility, gentleness and patience;

13 bearing with one another, and forgiving each other, whoever has a complaint against any one; just as the Lord forgave you, so also should you.

14 And beyond all these things put on love, which is the perfect bond of unity.

15 And let the peace of Christ rule in your hearts, to which indeed you were called in one body; and be thankful.

16 Let the word of Christ richly dwell within you, with all wisdom teaching and admonishing one another with psalms and hymns and spiritual songs, singing with thankfulness in your hearts to God.

17 And whatever you do in word or deed, do all in the name of the Lord Jesus, giving thanks through Him to God the Father.

TRUE SPIRITUALITY, Part 3

"Putting on the New"

Colossians 3:12-17

Wearing new clothes that fit and are stylish is a joy to every woman's heart. They lift our spirits and help us feel good about ourselves. The same is true in our spiritual lives. Galatians 3:27 tells us that as new creatures in Christ we have been clothed with Jesus himself. We are dressed in the most beautiful clothing in the universe, and they will never go out of style.

We are clothed with Christ because of our death and resurrection with Him. He is our life. This is foundational truth. But once again it needs to become experiential.

In Colossians 3:12-17, Paul shows us our "new clothes" in Christ. It is His wonderful character which we have living within. Now we need to wear them in our daily living.

These clothes fit perfectly. They may be foreign to our experience, but they are not to our spirits. Because of our identity with Christ, these "clothes" are the "real" us. When we go around in the rags of sin and the flesh, we're hiding the true beauty of our life in Christ. We're to dress in our true beauty and show forth the life of Christ within.

As we take a look at our "new clothes," we may not be used to the "style." We may feel more comfortable in our sinful rags. But we need to remind ourselves of the truth. Those rags, though familiar, no longer fit and are out of style. Our new clothes in Christ are an expression of our true selves and fit perfectly. (Remember once again that feelings are *not* necessarily truth.)

As you take a look in this lesson at Christ and realize that this is the life within you, may you begin more and more to experience the joy of wearing your new clothes. And may you grow to love and appreciate Christ as never before.

Study 1 – *A Heart of Compassion* (3:12)

1. Read the introduction and Colossians 3:12-17. (Underline what stands out to you.)

2. (a) How does Paul address new creatures in Christ in verse 12?

   (b) Why is this (2a) true of new creatures in Christ? Ephesians 1:4, 5; 2:4, 5: (cf. 2 Timothy 1:9; Romans 9:23, 24)

   (c) Meditate on these truths. Praise and thank God for them. What do they mean to you?

3. (a) Because of our death and resurrection with Christ, how is our life to manifest His life in us?
   Colossians 3:12

   (b) These things (3a) are not so much separate entities but qualities of life that are intertwined together. Read the following definitions carefully, underlining what stands out to you.

   compassion—deeply felt affection mixed with mercy, tenderheartedness

   kindness—goodness of heart, opposite of malice.

   humility—recognition of our total dependence on God for everything. A servant's heart in relationships. (A true understanding of the creature/creator relationship).

gentleness—also translated meekness. It is power under control. It is being dead to self; not defensive of one's own reputation but strongly defending God's reputation. Total submission to His will.

patience—bearing long with someone or something; not surrendering to circumstances or trials.

4. Since it is Christ's life in you that is to be manifested in these character qualities, what do you learn about His life in these areas from the following verses?

   (a) Compassion—Matthew 9:35-38 (cf. 14:13-21; 15:32-38; 20:29-34; 23:37; Psalm 103:13, 14)

   (b) Humility—John 13:1-5

   (c) Kindness—Luke 22:31, 32; (cf. Isaiah 40:11)

   (d) Gentleness (meekness)—Matthew 11:29; 26:49-56; (cf. John 6:38)

   (e) Patience—John 14:8-11 (cf. 16:12, 13)

5. (a) Meditate on what you've learned. Praise Christ for His person, His character, His heart. Thank Him that He lives within

you, that you are clothed with Him (Galatians 3:27). Ask God to sink this truth down deep into your heart.

(b) What situation(s) are you facing where you need to experience the power of Christ in you in one or more of these areas? How?

(c) Thank God that He is more than able to live out His character in and through you in this situation (5b). Ask Him for wisdom (insight) as to what steps you may need to take in living it out (James 1:5). Write down what He shows you.

(d) Are there any broken relationships in your life because you have failed to live out Christ's character in these areas? If so, confess it as sin to God, ask His forgiveness, and thank Him for it. Then go to that person and confess your sin and ask their forgiveness.

(e) Ask God to work His character deep into your experience in these areas. Ask Him to convict you when you are not living in light of whom you are.

6. How has your appreciation/understanding of Christ and His life in you grown from your study?

7. Begin memorizing Colossians 3:12-17.

Study 2 – *Forgiving One Another* (3:13)

1. Read Colossians 3:12-17.

2. In what ways are we to express the life of Christ according to verse 13?

3. (a) What do you learn about Christ's life in forgiving and bearing with others?

    John 8:1-11

    Luke 22:47, 48, 63-65; 23:32-34 (cf. Psalm 86:5)

   (b) What do you learn about His forgiving you from the following verses?

    Psalm 103:12
    Isaiah 43:25

4. (a) Meditate on what you've learned. Praise and thank Christ for His forgiveness. Thank Him that He lives within you. Thank Him that all of His character and power to forgive lives within you. Ask Him to work in your life that you might more and more live in this power and character in practice.

   (b) Is there anyone whom you have not forgiven for something? (Check yourself for bitterness, resentment. Is there someone you've pulled away from because they hurt you.)

(c) Confess your lack of forgiving as sin to God, ask His forgiveness, and thank Him for it. Then forgive that person. (Remember that this is based on the *fact* of your death to sin and your life in Christ, *not* your emotions.)

(d) If there have been barriers, coolness, distance in the relationship to that person, ask their forgiveness for your unforgiving spirit. Then let them know you forgive them.

(e) Prayerfully ask God to make you aware of any others whom you have not forgiven (bitterness, resentment, etc. towards another). Make a list of those God shows you. Then follow the same pattern (4b-d) with each one.

5. (a) How has this section affected your life?

   (b) How has your appreciation and/or understanding of Christ and His forgiveness grown from your study?

6. Continue memorizing Colossians 3:12-17.

Study 3 – *Love* (3:14)

1. Read Colossians 3:12-17.

2. What is another aspect of Christ's life that we are to express? (Verse 14)

3. (a) What do you learn about Christ's love from the following Scriptures?

   John 10:7-15 (cf. 1 John 3:16)

   John 13:1

   Romans 8:35-39

   *(b) Find an example of the list of love's characteristics in 1 Corinthians 13:4-8a. Find an example of one or more of them from the life of Christ in the Gospels.

   (c) Meditate on these truths. Praise and worship Christ. Thank Him for His love. Ask God to open your heart to appreciate and understand Christ's love in ever deeper degrees. Thank God that Christ's love lives within you. Ask God to work in your life that you might live out Christ's love in you.

   (d) What ministered to you most about Christ's love? How? Why?

(e) Asking God for insight, is there anyone you have failed to love with Christ's love? Confess your lack of love as sin to God, ask His forgiveness, and thank Him for it. Then go to that person and ask their forgiveness for your lack of love towards them.

*(f) Prayerfully before the Lord make a list of those in your life you have failed to love with Christ's love. Then follow the instructions in 3e.

(g) Asking God for insight, what steps do you need to take in becoming more and more a person characterized by Christ's love?

(h) Ask God to put what you wrote down in 3g deep into your habit pattern of life. Claim Ephesians 3:20.

4. Keep up the good work memorizing Colossians 3:12-17.

Study 4 – *Peace and the Word* (3:15, 16)

1. Read Colossians 3:12-17.

2. (a) What is to rule in our hearts? (Verse 15)

   (b) How does it rule in our hearts?
   Philippians 4:4-7

   *(c) How did Jesus exemplify peace in His own life? (Give examples of Philippians 4:4-7 from the life of Christ in the Gospels.)

3. (a) Meditate on what you've learned. Praise and thank Christ for His peace. What stands out to you about Christ's peace? Why?

   (b) Has His peace ruled in your life?

   If yes—praise and thank Him.

   If no—confess your failure as sin to God, ask His forgiveness, and thank Him for it.

   (c) Prayerfully review Philippians 4:4-7. What steps do you need to take for Christ's peace to rule in your life?

   (d) Ask God to work what you wrote down in 3c into your habit pattern of living. Claim Ephesians 3:20.

4. (a) What place is the Word to have in our lives? (Verse 16a)

   (b) What will be the result in our lives? (Verse 16b)

5. (a) How did the Scriptures dwell in Christ richly?

   Matthew 4:1-11 (cf. 15:1-9; 22:34-46)

   (b) Why did they dwell in Christ richly? Isaiah 50:4, 5

   (c) Meditate on these truths. How does your life need to reflect Christ's in this area?

   (d) Ask God to work what you wrote down in 5d deep into your life. Claim Ephesians 3:20 for this area of your life.

6. How has your appreciation and/or understanding of Christ grown from your study of this section?

7. Don't get discouraged. Keep memorizing Colossians 3:12-17. (You have three weeks to work on it!)

Study 5 – *Singing, Doing, and Thanking* (3:15-17)

1. Read Colossians 3:12-17.

2. (a) How are we to sing to God? (Verse 16)
   (b) What do the Scriptures tell us about Jesus and singing?
       Mark 14:26 (Notice the context.)
       Hebrews 2:12
   *(c) What do you learn about the occasions, importance, and/or content of singing to the Lord from the following Scriptures?
       Exodus 14:26—15:18
       1 Chronicles 6:31, 32
       Psalm 33:1-4 (cf. 92:1-4; 105:2, 3)
       Psalm 57:1-11
   (d) Review what you've learned. What stands out to you about the importance of singing?
   (e) How do these truths need to affect your life?
   (f) Spend time today singing to God. Ask Him to make it a habit pattern of your life.

3. (a) How are we to live our lives? (Verse 17)
   (b) "Name" in the Bible refers to one's person and character.
   (c) How did Jesus live in the name of His Father?
       John 4:34 (cf. John 5:19, 30;6:38; 12:49; 14:10)
       John 15:9
       John 17:4, 6

(d) Meditate on what you've learned. Praise Christ for His character and life. Thank Him that He lives within you. Ask God to work in your life to live as Christ did. Ask Him to convict you where you have not.

(e) Where you have not lived in accordance with these truths, confess it as sin to God, ask His forgiveness, and thank Him for it.

(f) Asking God for insight, how does your life need to be affected by these truths?

(g) Ask God to work what you wrote down in 3f deep into your life. Claim Ephesians 3:20.

4. (a) What do Colossians 3:15-17 all say is to be part of our lives?

(b) What does the repetition in each verse tell you about its importance?

(c) Spend some time being obedient to these exhortations to thanksgiving. Ask God to make it a habit pattern of your life.

*(d) How did Jesus exemplify this life style? (Give examples from the Gospels.)

5. (a) Remember, Christ lives in you to empower your living in each of these areas. Thank Him.

(b) How has your appreciation and/or understanding of Christ grown from your study of this section?

*6. How has your understanding of the life within you (your new clothes) grown from your study of this lesson (Studies 1-5)?

*7. How has this lesson (Studies 1-5) encouraged your walk with Christ?

18 Wives, be subject to your husbands, as is fitting in the Lord.

19 Husbands, love your wives, and do not be embittered against them.

20 children, be obedient to your parents in all things, for this is well-pleasing to the Lord.

21 Fathers, do not exasperate your children, that they may not lose heart.

22 Slaves, in all things obey those who are your masters on earth, not with external service, as those who merely please men, but with sincerity of heart, fearing the Lord.

23 Whatever you do, do your work heartily, as for the Lord rather than for men;

24 knowing that from the Lord you will receive the reward of the inheritance. It is the Lord Christ whom you serve.

25 For he who does wrong will receive the consequences of the wrong which he has done, and that without partiality.

1 Masters, grant to your slaves justice and fairness, knowing that you too have a Master in heaven.

TRUE SPIRITUALITY, Part 4

"Family Relationships"

Colossians 3:18—4:1

Probably the hardest place to live the Christian life is in the home. That's where we let down. That's where the raw edges show. That's where true spirituality is put to the acid test.

How can we pass this test? Again we have to go back to the foundation of our spiritual lives. There is no way to bring glory to God in our family relationships unless we base our home living on our death and resurrection with Christ. God's instructions for family living cannot be obeyed except by His power.

God is a God of order and peace. He set up the universe to run smoothly by "natural laws." He set up the church to function in an orderly manner. He's given specific instructions to wives, husbands, children, and parents so the family might do the same.

But it is impossible to live in obedience to God's orders for the family apart from His life within. As the Son was submissive to the Father here on earth, so women can be submissive to their husbands. As Christ loved the church, so husbands must love their wives. As God disciplines, trains, and lovingly relates to His children, so parents can with theirs. Since Christ is our life, obedience is possible.

The same principles of life you learned in lessons 7 and 8 are needed to learn obedience to the commands of Colossians 3:18—4:1. No amount of self-effort will get the job done. It takes a death to our old sinful habit patterns of thinking and living, and then a learning of obedience as we walk in the power and awareness of the new life within. We have to once again learn in reality the truth of our death and resurrection with Christ. We begin living as who we really are.

Some who do this lesson may be single. Others have no children at home. If the commands of Scripture do not directly apply to you, learn God's truth that you may help others in the body of Christ.

May you begin to experience in deeper and deeper measure true spirituality at home as a result of your study.

Study 1 – *Wives and Husbands* (3:18)

1. Read the introduction (Underline what stands out to you.)
   and Colossians 3:18—4:1.

2. (a) What is the command to the wife in verse 18?

   (b) Define subject (synonym: submit).

   (c) List the reason(s) why (1) you aren't subject to your husband, (2) you feel you can't be subject to your husband, and/or (3) you don't want to be subject to your husband.

3. (a) What are God's reasons why you are to be subject to your husband?

      Ephesians 5:22-24 (cf.1 Corinthians 11:3; 1 Corinthians 14:33, 40)

      1 Peter 3:1, 2 (cf. 1 Peter 3:3-6)

   (b) Meditate on what you learned in 3a. What stands out to you?

   (c) Review what you wrote down in 2c. What has shaped your thinking and living in this area—God's Word or the world's philosophy (humanism, etc.)? How?

   (d) Confess as sin to God where your thinking and living have not been in conformity to His Word in relationship to your husband. Ask His forgiveness and thank Him for it. Ask God to renew your mind, emotions, and life in His truth in this area.

(e) Where your life has reflected God's truth in submitting to your husband, praise and thank God for His work in you.

(f) If you have not been subject to your husband, go to him and confess your sin and ask his forgiveness.

(g) How can you live in obedience to God's Word in this area?

Romans 6:11-13 (cf. 6:1-10)
Romans 12:2
Colossians 3:1-3

(h) Ask God to work in your life in this area. Praise Him for what He's going to do. Claim Ephesians 3:20.

4. (a) What difference in your thinking and living has your study of this section made in your life?

*(b) How could you begin to teach your daughter (or younger women you know) these truths?

5. Don't forget to keep working on memorizing Colossians 3:12-17.

Study 2 – *Husbands and Wives* (3:19)

1. Read Colossians 3:18—4:1.

2. (a) What is God's first command to the husband in verse 19?

   (b) How is he to do this (2a)?
   Ephesians 5:25, 33 (cf. 1 Corinthians
   13:4-8a)

   1 Peter 3:8

   (c) Pray for your husband that he will walk
   in obedience to God. (Remember that it
   takes as much dependence on God for
   your husband to love you like this as it
   does for you to submit yourself to him.)
   Claim Ephesians 3:20.

   (d) If your husband is not a new creature in
   Christ, remember 1 Peter 3:1, 2. Claim
   it in prayer before God.

   (e) Meditate on what you've learned. Praise
   and thank God for how He wants to love
   you through your husband.

   (f) Thank your husband today for one way
   he loves you in which you can see or feel
   Christ's love.

3. (a) What is God's second command to the
   husband in Colossians 3:19?

(b) Why could a husband be embittered against his wife?

Proverbs 11:22

Proverbs 12:4

Proverbs 21:9, 19 (cf. Proverbs 19:13; 25:24; 27:15, 16)

(c) Is there any reason your husband could be embittered against you?

If yes, confess your sin to God, ask His forgiveness, and thank Him for it. Then confess your sin to your husband and ask his forgiveness.

4. (a) What effect on your life has this section had?

(b) How has your appreciation of your husband and his God-given responsibility grown from your study of this section?

(c) How has your understanding of God and marriage grown from your study of Studies 1 and 2?

*(d) How could you instruct your sons in the truths you discovered in this section?

Study 3 – *Children and Parents* (3:20)

1. Read again Colossians 3:18—4:1.

2. (a) What is the command to children? (Verse 20)

   (b) Why are they to obey this command? (Verse 20)

3. (a) How can you teach your children obedience? (If you have no children or yours are grown, learn God's instructions to share with others.)

      Proverbs 13:24 (cf. 22:15; 23:13, 14; 29:15)

      Proverbs 22:6

   (b) Why do children have to be taught obedience?
      Jeremiah 17:9 (cf. Proverbs 22:15a; 29:15b)

   (c) What will the result be if you teach your child obedience (for your child and for you)?

      Proverbs 15:31 (cf. Proverbs 10:17a)

      Proverbs 29:17 (cf. Proverbs 23:15, 16, 24)

(d) What is the result if your child does not learn obedience?

Proverbs 10:1 (cf. 17:25)

Proverbs 10:17b

Proverbs 13:18a

Proverbs 29:15

4. (a) Meditate on what you've learned. Ask God to make these truths sink down into your thinking and living. What stands out to you from these truths? Why?

(b) For those with younger children, asking God for insight, how do these truths need to be applied to your childrearing?

(c) For those without younger children, is there anyone you could encourage by sharing these truths with them? Who?

(d) As a child, were you disobedient or rebellious? Are there any rifts in the relationship between you and your parents because of past rebellion?

If you've never confessed your sin to God and asked His forgiveness, do so now.

If you've never made it right with your parents, confess your sin to them and ask their forgiveness.

Study 4 – *Parents and Children* (3:21)

1. Read Colossians 3:18—4:1.

2. (a) What is the exhortation to fathers (parents) in verse 21?

   (b) What is the reason for this exhortation? Colossians 3:21

*3. (a) What do you learn about God our Father's dealings with us in Psalm 103:7-14 which could help you discipline and relate to your children?

   (b) Praise God for His heart. Ask Him to give you a heart like His.

4. Discover truths in the following verses which can help you learn to correct, discipline, train, and relate to your children without exasperating them or making them lose heart.

   Proverbs 3:5, 6 (cf. Proverbs 11:2 16:18; 26:12; 28:25)

   Proverbs 12:15

   Proverbs 12:18 (cf. Proverbs 10:19; 15:4; 16:24; 17:27; 21:23; 29:20)

   Proverbs 15:1

   Proverbs 15:28

Proverbs 24:23

5. (a) Meditate on what you've learned. Ask God to convict you in the areas in which you need to change, where you need to be conformed to His Word. Ask Him to transform your life in these areas. Claim Ephesians 3:20. (Be sure to confess any disobedience as sin to God, ask His forgiveness, and thank Him for it. Do the same with your child.)

   (b) Which truth(s) or principle(s) of relationship do you most need to put into practice with your children? Why? How?

6. (a) What stood out to you in your study of this section?

   *(b) Give a summary of Biblical parenting from Studies 3 and 4.

7. Don't forget about memorizing Colossians 3:12-17.

Study 5 – *Job Relationships* (3:22 – 4:1)

1. Read Colossians 3:18—4:1.

2. In Paul's day, slaves were part of the home life. Though we are not slaves today with masters, the principles Paul shares here are applicable to our jobs, another place our walk with Christ is put to the test.

3. (a) What is the general principle we are to follow whenever we have a job to do? Colossians 3:22, 23
   (b) What job(s) do you have?
   (c) Have you been obedient to Colossians 3:23 in your job(s)? How or how not?
   (d) Where you have been obedient to Colossians 3:23, give thanks to God for His work in you and through you.
   (e) Why are you to be obedient to Colossians 3:23? Colossians 3:24, 25
   (f) Asking God for insight, what steps do you need to take for your life to be conformed to Colossians 3:23-25?

4. (a) If you have a place of authority in a job, how should you treat those under you? Colossians 4:1
   (b) Why are you to treat them this way? Colossians 4:1
   (c) How do these truths need to affect your life?

2 Devote yourselves to prayer, keeping alert in it with an attitude of thanksgiving;

3 praying at the same time for us as well, that God may open up to us a door for the word, so that we may speak forth the mystery of Christ, for which I have also been imprisoned;

4 in order that I may make it clear in the way I ought to speak.

5 Conduct yourselves with wisdom toward outsiders, making the most of the opportunity.

6 Let your speech always be with grace, seasoned, as it were, with salt, so that you may know how you should respond to each person.

7 As to all my affairs, Tychicus, our beloved brother and faithful servant and fellow-bondslave in the Lord, will bring you information.

8 For I have sent him to you for this very purpose, that you may know about our cirucmstances and that he may encourage your hearts;

9 and with him Onesimus, our faithful and beloved brother, who is one of your number. They will inform you about the whole situation here.

10 Aristarchus, my fellow prisoner, sends you his greetings; and also Barnabas' cousin Mark (about whom you received instructions; if he comes to you, welcome him);

11 and also Jesus who is called Justus; these are the only fellow-workers for the kingdom of God who are from the circumcision; and they have proved to be an encouragement to me.

12 Epaphras, who is one of your number, a bondslave of Jesus Christ, sends you his greetings, always laboring earnestly for you in his prayers, that you may stand perfect and fully assured in all the will of God.

13 For I bear him witness that he has a deep concern for you and for those who are in Laodicea nd Hierapolis.

14 Luke, the beloved physician, sends you his greetings, and also Demas.

15 Greet the brethren who are in Laodicea and also Nympha and the church that is in her house.

16 And when this letter is read among you, have it also read in the church of the Laodiceans; and you, for your part read my letter that is coming from Laodicea.

17 And say to Archippus, "Take heed to the ministry which you have received in the Lord, that you may fulfill it."

18 I, Paul, write this greeting with my own hand. Remember my imprisonment. Grace be with you.

THREE SPIRITUAL ESSENTIALS

Colossians 4:2-18

For the sustaining of physical life there are a few essentials. We must have food, water, and, in most climates, clothing and shelter. Without these our physical lives will wither away. They are vital for strength and health.

There are also essentials for the health of our spiritual lives. As Paul closes his letter to the Colossians, he mentions three of them—prayer, witnessing, and strong relationships within the body of Christ. These are imperative for a vital spiritual existence.

Paul does not share these essentials in a doctrinal dissertation, but by opening his heart and life to us. As he shares personally, we get a glimpse at three essentials of a healthy Christian life.

May you glean from these verses spiritual sustenance for the maintaining of a vital life in Christ. And as you look back at your study of Colossians, may you be strengthened and encouraged by all God has taught you and done in you.

Study 1 – *The Importance of Prayer* (4:2)

1. Read the introduction and Colossians 4:2-18.

2. What three things are to characterize our prayer lives according to verse 2?

3. (a) Define devote.

   (b) Why is it important for us to be devoted to prayer?

      1 Samuel 12:23

      Luke 18:1

      1 Peter 4:7

4. Why do we need to stay alert when we pray?

   Matthew 26:41

   1 Peter 5:8

5. Why is it important to have an attitude of thanksgiving when we pray?

   Psalm 100:4, 5

6. (a) Meditate on what you've learned. Ask God to make it sink down deep into your heart, mind, and life. What stands out to you most in these truths about prayer?

(b) Have you been obedient to God's Word in your prayer life? How or how not? (Be sure to confess as sin to God any disobedience, ask His forgiveness, and thank Him for it.)

(c) Asking God for insight, what do you need to do to be obedient to God's Word in your prayer life?

7. Continue memorizing Colossians 3:12-17.

Study 2 – *The Importance of Prayer* (**4:3, 4**)

1. Read Colossians 4:2-18.

2. (a) What prayer requests does Paul make in verses 3 and 4? (Paul makes these requests near the end of his life.)

   (b) Read at least one of the following passages in Acts and notice Paul's skill and boldness in telling others about Christ. Jot down what stands out to you.
   Acts 9:20-22; 13:16-42; 17:22-33; 26:1-29

   (c) Prayerfully review 2a and 2b. In light of what you've learned, what do Paul's requests in verses 3 and 4 tell you about the importance and need of prayer in our lives?

   (d) In light of what you've learned in 2a and 2b, how important is prayer to our witness?

   *(e) Compare Colossians 4:3, 4 with John 15:5.

   (f) Asking God for insight, how do you need to apply these truths to your life?

3. Keep up the good work on Colossians 3:12-17.

Study 3 – *Wisdom in Witnessing* (4:5, 6)

1. Read Colossians 4:2-18.

2. (a) In verses 3 and 4, Paul asked for prayer for his witness. In verses 5 and 6, he exhorts the Colossians to be effective in their witness.

   (b) What are the two exhortations Paul gives in verses 5 and 6?

   (c) What reasons does he give for his exhortations? (Verses 5, 6)

3. (a) How can we conduct ourselves with wisdom toward those who don't know Christ? James 1:5

   (b) What characterizes wise conduct? James 3:13-18

4. (a) How can our speech be seasoned with grace and salt in our witness?

   Ephesians 4:15 (cf. 1 Peter 3:15)

   Ephesians 4:29

   *(b) Give an explanation of the "hope that is in you" based on God's Word.

5. Why is it important to make the most of our opportunities to share Christ with those who don't know Him?

   Romans 13:11, 12a; (cf. Ephesians 5:15, 16)

6. (a) Meditate on what you've learned. What stands out to you about sharing Christ with those who don't know Him?

   (b) Has your witness for Christ reflected these truths?

      If yes—thank God for what He's done in and through you.

      If no—confess your failure as sin to God, ask His forgiveness, and thank Him for it.

   (c) Asking God for insight, how do these truths need to affect your life and witness?

7. Don't forget to review Colossians 3:12-17.

Study 4 – *Body Relationships* (4:7-18)

1. Read Colossians 4:2-18.

2. From Colossians 4:7-18 what do you learn about the following:

   (a) The importance of relationships in the body of Christ.

   (b) The benefits of relationships in the body of Christ.

   (c) Our need of relationships in the body of Christ.

   (d) How we build relationships in the body of Christ.

3. (a) Prayerfully review what you've learned. Praise and thank God for these truths.

   (b) Which truths you discovered in 2a, b, c, and d have you experienced? How?

   (c) Asking God for insight, how do you need to grow in your relationships with your brothers and sisters in Christ?

   (d) Praise and thank God for the things you wrote down in 3b. Ask God to work deep into your life and living the things you wrote down in 3c.

4. How are you doing memorizing Colossians 3:12-17?

Study 5 – *Review Colossians* (1-4)

1. What truth(s) that you have learned in your study of Colossians has meant the most to you? Why? How?

2. How has your life changed from your study of Colossians?

3. What is the greatest need(s) you see in your life because of your study of Colossians?

4. Praise and thank God for the things you wrote down in questions 1 and 2. Ask God to work deeply in your life about what you wrote down in question 3. Claim Ephesians 3:20!

5. Can you say Colossians 3:12-17 from memory?

GUIDELINES FOR LEADERS

You don't learn to be a discussion leader in a vacuum. The learning takes place in the doing—the trial and error, days of success and days that are not so successful. But God is faithful. He prods us to grow day by day, and I am thankful for that.

Let's take a look at some general principles of leading a discussion group and ways of organizing your women's Bible study. I share these not as an "expert," but as one who is learning like you in the school of practical experience. I must also note that I am deeply indebted to Pat Smith, who has shared with me her years of experience in Bible Study Fellowship and as coordinator of the Women's Bible Study in my home church. I pray that you will find encouragement and assistance in the suggestions that follow.

Colossians can be either a ten or twelve-week study. Lessons 2 and 8 are lengthy and can be divided easily into two-week studies. If you have mothers with young children or women who are short on time, you may want to take two weeks to cover each lesson.

Ideas for Class Organization

1. Discussion Group/Lecture
This works well in groups of twenty or more. The women can be divided into groups of eight to twelve. After the lesson is discussed in small groups, the ladies come together for a teaching time on the passage. Sample agenda:

(a) Opening (announcements, singing, coffee time	15 minutes
(b) Discussion group time	1—1¼ hours
(c) Lecture/teaching	30—40 minutes

You can vary the times to suit your needs. In this setup, the teaching leader can meet with the discussion leaders beforehand to cover the lesson and pray together.

2. Discussion Group

This works best for small groups (8-15). The leader can give a small summary at the end of the discussion. The amount of time spent will depend on the needs and desires of your group. You will need at least an hour to cover the material.

Choosing Discussion Leaders

Here are some things to think about when choosing a leader: (1) A discussion leader must be committed to Christ and be willing to commit herself unconditionally to love the women in her group as unto the Lord. (2) Being a discussion leader costs in time and energy. (3) A discussion leader is *not* a teacher, but a *guide* of the discussion. Just because a woman is outgoing does not mean she will be a good discussion leader. A good discussion leader must be able to control her talking and focus on drawing out others. (4) A discussion leader does not need to be a Bible scholar, but evidence of maturity in Christ is very important.

Purpose of a Discussion Group

A discussion group has a threefold purpose. One is to strengthen it in Bible knowledge. The discussion helps to solidify what is learned in personal study. The discussion time also gives incentive to finish the lesson.

The second purpose is to build up the body of Christ. Strong bonds grow as we openly share our lives and pray for one another. When one shares how God is teaching her, it spurs the rest of the group on. As we share what God is doing in our lives, we stimulate one another to love and good deeds (Hebrew 10:24).

It is important in a discussion group to keep both of these purposes in focus and in balance. Each purpose must be equally important if there is to be success.

A third purpose is worship. Praise God together for what you learned of Him and His ways. You can do this by conversational prayer, singing, and adoring the Lord together.

Practical Suggestions for Leaders

1. Personal Preparation

Our own personal time with God is the most important aspect of being a discussion leader. Leading a group is not so much "doing" the right thing as "being" the right person. The spirit we bring to the discussion time sets the tone. Our spirit is dependent on our times of quietness alone with God during the week.

As God works in our lives, and as we come to know Him, then we have something to share with the women. God is free to love and work through us. In no way do we have to be perfect or "have it all together." The women in the group need our honesty—our failures as well as our victories. They need to sense the reality of our walk with God and His Spirit within us. We won't necessarily be conscious of this. Second Corinthians 3:18 says that as we look at Him He transforms us into His image by the work of His Spirit. Our responsibility is to spend time with Him in His Word. He'll be faithful to do His part and the women in the group will reap the benefit.

God's ministry is just that—His. He will be faithful in working through us as we are faithful in walking with Him—even if it seems like we're doing the five step, three steps forward and two steps back!

Prayer is a vital part of our preparation. As we pray specifically for the women and the discussion time, we have the joy of seeing God's power displayed in answered prayer. Prayer is also the key to unconditional love. We don't always feel loving. Loving takes time, energy, and self-sacrifice. Often there are women in the group who are difficult to love naturally. As we honestly pour out our souls to God in prayer (Psalm 62:8), we begin to experience God's transforming power in our love. It is important to remember that love is not just feelings. Often it is only as we take steps of obedience to God's Word to do the loving thing (reach out, spend time, forgive, etc.) that our feelings are transformed. But it all begins with prayer.

Lesson preparation is another essential for the discussion leader. The better we know the lesson, the freer we are to guide the discussion and respond to the needs of the women.

Spend time daily in study. It helps tremendously. Then at the end of the week review—a thorough review helps to solidify all we've learned.

2. Phone Calls

One way to be sensitive to the needs of the women is to call them periodically *(every week or two)*. This takes a commitment of time, but is very rewarding. As we ask questions to get to know them, and share ourselves with them, a relationship grows. They have the opportunity to share their needs with us. If they're having difficulty with the lesson, we can give assistance. Everyone needs to be loved and cared for. Our phone calls are one way to show the women that we care.

3. Group Luncheons

A luncheon *(maybe one every six weeks)* gives the women in the group an opportunity to get to know each other better. They can be held in a home, at the church, or in a restaurant—variety is nice. Have some "get-to-know-you" questions to break the ice. "How did you meet your husband?" or "What do you look for in a friend?" A few questions are good to get the women to share their joys, hurts, and desires.

4. Opening

The impression a woman gets when she walks through the door to the study is crucial. A friendly smile and warm greeting are vital. She needs to know immediately that she is wanted. For many it is a very threatening experience. It is all important that each woman feels accepted and significant.

This responsibility need not rest solely on the leader's shoulders. Recruit others to help.

(a) Name tags are also a good tool to promote a warm atmosphere. Remembering a person's name is extremely important for their self-worth. But remembering a lot of names is difficult. Name tags will solve this problem and put everyone on a first name basis.

(b) One way to make a newcomer feel at home is to ask one of the regulars to see her through the day—sit with her, introduce her to others, be her friend.

(c) Coffee and goodies can help to create a warm atmosphere.

(d) Begin with a few worship choruses to help focus attention on the Lord. These should not be heavy hymns, but simple songs that turn our hearts to our Father and Savior.

5. Prayer Time

Spend the first fifteen minutes of the discussion time in sharing prayer requests and praying. Prayer helps to build strong cords of love among the women. As we pray for one another and see God's answers, our faith grows. Encourage the women to share not only physical needs but also spiritual and emotional ones. This is an important aspect in fulfilling the purpose of the discussion group.

6. Guiding the Discussion

(a) As discussion leaders, we must always remember that our purpose is to guide, not dominate. Our desire is to draw out what the women have learned in God's Word. The Bible is the authority; the Holy Spirit is the teacher. If we supply "the answers," it stops discussion. The women need to know that what they've learned is important to us. We all are in a sense teaching one another as we share what we've learned together.

(b) Allow the women to volunteer their answers. Don't be afraid to wait a few moments for them to respond. Always asking someone for answers makes for dull discussion.

(c) We need to listen carefully to each woman. Eye contact is important to good listening. Our full attention needs to be focused on the one who is sharing. We must be careful not to interrupt her by words, mental wondering, or body movements.

(d) A warm and sincere response helps to assure a woman of her worth, and the worth of what she's shared. Here are some sample responses:

"I appreciate that."

"That's really encouraging."

"I identify with that."

"You really applied that truth."

"That's great! I hadn't thought of that."

"Thanks for sharing that."

"You have a beautiful spirit."

"Thanks!"

"God really ministered that to you."

It is important to remember that the answers be *sincere.* Praise and appreciation are welcomed by all of us, but they must be sincere. We need to ask God to give us a genuine appreciation for the women and what they share.

(e) Sometimes to answer a question a woman will share a hurt or difficulty in her life. It's good at those times to stop and have someone pray for her specifically. Don't leave a hurt hanging—a short prayer helps lift the load. It also goes a long way towards building a loving, caring group.

(f) As discussion leaders it is best to let others answer first. The one exception is personal application questions. If the women seem hesitant to share openly, we may need to take the lead. Openness breeds openness. If we are willing to be honest and vulnerable, the women will be more apt to do the same. Sharing on the personal level grows us into more than just a discussion group—into a caring, loving community.

(g) Open sharing does not mean gossip. To guard against this, do not share anything about another person that you wouldn't share if they were present. Open sharing is sharing our own personal joys or struggles—not someone else's.

(h) The discussion time should flow—neither rushing or dragging our heels. Dividing the lesson in half beforehand, and knowing what time we should arrive at the halfway point, can help in getting through the entire lesson in the time allotted. But we need to be sensitive to the Holy Spirit. There may be a question God has used deeply in a number of lives. Don't be afraid to spend the time needed. It is important to cover the entire lesson, but it is also important to allow the Spirit freedom to work. A real balance is needed here. We need to ask God for wisdom as we lead. If we see that there won't be enough time to finish all the questions, just cover the key questions. (Mark these out beforehand.) Let the women know if they have questions on any that you've skipped, you'll be glad to cover them after the study is over.

(i) Keep a sense of humor. It is not a deadly serious task. We should enjoy our time together. As Proverbs 17:22 says, "A joyful heart is good medicine." Laughter is a wonderful part of our time together.

7. Possible Problems

You may be saying, "This all sounds nice, but what do I do if . . .?"

(a) What do I do with the extremely shy woman? Never force a shy woman to share. For some just sitting there takes all the courage they can muster. Putting pressure on them can scare them away. They need to be treated very gently. The phone calls can be a great help. Ask them about the lesson and, if they share, let them know how much it meant. Then ask them if they'd be willing to share it with the group. Always remember to be sensitive to their fears and *gently* draw them out.

(b) What do I do with the woman who talks all the time? It is important to gently limit her contributions so all the women have a chance to share. One way to do this is to ask that someone who hasn't shared yet answer the question. It's important not to reprimand an over talkative member in the group. If it becomes a serious problem, talk with her outside of class. Maybe meet for lunch one day. Let her know how much you appreciate her input, and how valuable it is. Share with her that some of the women have a more difficult time opening up or have less knowledge. She could assist you by giving them a little more opportunity to participate. This is an area that needs to be bathed in our personal prayer time during the week.

(c) What if someone gives a "wrong" answer? Again, sensitivity is needed. Though we should never say "that's wrong," we shouldn't let a wrong answer pass without clarification. A couple of ways to handle this are: (1) solicit others to add their answers, then give a summary leaving out the incorrect answer; (2) go to God's Word. Open it up together and let it be the authority. Whether a woman's answer is correct or not, let her know she's appreciated.

(d) What if I'm asked a question I don't know? Don't panic. We don't have to "know it all." We can ask if anyone else in the group knows the answer. If not, we can let them know it's a good question, and we'll give more time and study to it during the coming week.

(e) What if someone asks a question or makes a statement that can lead to a tangent? Let them know though it's an interesting topic, it will have to be pursued at another time—maybe at a luncheon if everyone seems interested.

(f) What if no one has done their lesson? Spend time doing some of it together.

8. Evaluating Your Time

The best time to evaluate how your discussion group is doing is *not* right afterwards. Usually we're tired then, and that always colors the think-ing. Sometime during the week check up on your-self:

Is there a warm atmosphere?

How's the timing coming?

Am I being open? Are the women?

Was I prepared?

How're my listening skills?

Are my shy gals sharing more?

Are the talkers under control?

Don't just zero in on the negatives. Praise and thank God for the positives and progress. Ask Him for wisdom in the areas that need work. Re-member, He is growing us in this area of ministry. Thank Him for the privilege; thank Him for using you.

The Lesson

In discussing the lesson, it is not necessary to discuss every question. In the preface to the study the types of questions are listed. Most of the #1 questions and some of the #2 questions can be summarized by you or can be covered by going quickly around the circle. The #3 and #4 ques-tions make for the best discussion.

At the end of some sections, there is a question like, "What stood out to you most in this section." Instead of going through all the questions and then going back over them again in personal sharing, cover the section with that one question. But in doing this, it is important that the women tie their personal sharing in with the specific question, verse, and answer that stood out to them.

To begin the discussion time, you may want to use the introduction of the lesson as your springboard. You can pull out a point, summarize it, share something that stood out to you, or ask the women what stood out to them. The introduction can help bring into focus where you're going as you start the discussion time.

Remember to write any notes you need in your book so you can easily guide the discussion. Mark the questions for discussion with a see-through marking pen. Some of the questions for discussion follow "Meditate ..." or "Pray...." Just cover the question part in discussion.

May God richly bless you in your time together.